USING
DESIGNED EXPERIMENTS
TO SHRINK
HEALTH CARE COSTS

USING
DESIGNED EXPERIMENTS
TO SHRINK
HEALTH CARE COSTS

M. Daniel Sloan

ASQC Quality Press
Milwaukee, Wisconsin

Using Designed Experiments to Shrink Health Care Costs
M. Daniel Sloan

Library of Congress Cataloging-in-Publication Data
Sloan, M. Daniel, 1950–
    Using designed experiments to shrink health care costs / M. Daniel
Sloan.
      p. cm.
    Includes bibliographical references and index.
    ISBN 0-87389-367-0 (alk. paper)
    1. Medical care—Quality control—Mathematical models.   2. Medical
care—Quality control—Mathematical models.   I. Title.
    [DNLM: 1. Cost Control—methods.   2. Mathematics.   3. Health Care
Costs.   W 74 S6345u   1997]
RA410.S56   1997
338.4'33621—dc20
DNLM/DLC
for Library of Congress   96-17217
                                                    CIP

Trademark Acknowledgment
K'NEX® is a registered trademark of K'NEX Industries, Inc.

10 9 8 7 6 5 4 3 2 1

ISBN 0-87389-367-0

Acquisitions Editor: Kelley Cardinal
Project Editor: Kelley Cardinal

Cover illustration, crystal (Figure 1.9), the IDEA cycle (Figures 1.11 and 8.1), layers of soil (Figure 2.21), layers of skin (Figure 2.22), bureaucratic pyramids (Figure 8.2), and molecular organizational design model (Figure 8.3) by John Pendleton. Photography (Figures 2.24, 2.27, 3.1, 6.5, and 7.2) by Shel Izen.

ASQC Mission: To facilitate continuous improvement and increase customer satisfaction by identifying, communicating, and promoting the use of quality principles, concepts, and technologies; and thereby be recognized throughout the world as the leading authority on, and champion for, quality.

Attention: Schools and Corporations
ASQC Quality Press books, audiotapes, videotapes, and software are available at quantity discounts with bulk purchases for business, educational, or instructional use. For information, please contact ASQC Quality Press at 800-248-1946, or write to ASQC Quality Press, P.O. Box 3005, Milwaukee, WI 53201-3005.

For a free copy of the ASQC Quality Press Publications Catalog, including ASQC membership information, call 800-248-1946.

Printed in the United States of America

 Printed on acid-free paper

Quality Press
611 East Wisconsin Avenue
Milwaukee, Wisconsin 53202

Many of the most useful designs are extremely simple.

Sir Ronald Aylmer Fisher

In treating patients with unproved remedies we are, whether we like it or not, experimenting on human beings, and a good experiment well reported may be more ethical and entail less shirking of duty than a poor one.

Sir Austin Bradford Hill
Quoting the editor of the *British Medical Journal*
The Clinical Trial, *New England Journal of Medicine*

Philosophy [natural philosophy, or science] is written in this grand book, the universe, which stands continually open to our gaze; [but this book] cannot be understood unless one first learns to comprehend the language and read the letters in which it is composed. It is written in the language of mathematics, and its characters are triangles, circles, and other geometric figures without which it is humanly impossible to understand a single word of it.

Galileo
The Assayer

Contents

Preface

If you are in a hurry to learn how to improve health care quality and shrink health care costs, turn to the fast-track experiments beginning on page 49. Use the prepared data. In *less than 15 minutes*, you will be able to correctly identify important factors and a two-factor interaction for a two-level, three-factor, 2^3 factorial experimental design. No algebra. No statistics. No computers. No fooling.

This book is for you if you enjoy solving the puzzles posed by your work quickly, efficiently, correctly, and imaginatively. By any measure, you will find designed experiments are more than you bargained for. When you have completed this book's self-study examples, you will have an entirely improved world view. You will know how to use a truly astonishing method to vastly improve the quality of your decisions. You will understand the paradox of simple complexity.

Nurses, doctors, therapists, health care managers, psychologists, health insurance executives, and hospital executives will find that designed experiment decision tools are indispensable. If you are a parent with a skeptical high school student or undergraduate who asks, "When will I ever use algebra, geometry, the scientific method, or statistics in real life?" use this book to demonstrate the correct answer is, "Absolutely every day!"

Designed experiments produce high-quality information. With designed experiments, high-quality information can and often does lead to well-reasoned decisions. Knowledge and insight, rewards in their own right, shrink the human and financial costs of delivering health care services.

Designed experiments work well with any number of variables in any number of professions. Medicine, nursing, respiratory therapy, physiology, pharmacology, agriculture, horticulture, astronomy, nutrition, financial management, accounting, dietetics, psychology, aerospace engineering, or any other professional activity provides excellent subject matter for inexpensive and productive designed experiment studies. The design of experiments can help you produce results with your qualitative and quantitative data. Plus, it is fun!

Logic supports the use of math and science in health care and in every aspect of business management. The line of reasoning is simple.

Any person who uses data—counts and measures—must use arithmetic. Algebra promotes a higher level of reasoning than addition, subtraction, division, and multiplication. Algebra, the language used for statistical reasoning, affords a more complete analysis of data than arithmetic. Every algebraic equation can be graphed using geometry. Pictures, geometry's gift, make difficult numbers easy to understand. Personal computers make the daily use of algebra, geometry, and meaningful statistical pictures as convenient as a mouse click.

The arguments against using math and science on a daily basis in health care and business management are absurd. Everybody who did their homework in medical school and nursing school knows that in 1924 Willem Einthoven was awarded the Nobel Prize for medicine for having invented the electrocardiograph (EKG) in 1908. The EKG strip is created using elementary algebra and geometry—small sample statistics.

The x, y, and z orthogonal planes in the Fisher/Box experimental cube are called the sagittal (x), horizontal (y), and frontal (z) orthogonal planes in Einthoven's reference frame. The geometry of the orthogonal planes in a 2^3 design allows the scientist, physician, or nurse to take only one or two sample heartbeats from the thousands of daily heartbeats and interpret the patterns of variation over time.[1] A vector analysis is a vector analysis.

Experience teaches nothing without theory. Just because you are up and running, improving health care quality, and shrinking health care costs in 15 minutes is no reason to stop learning. Designed experimentation is a challenging curriculum. In all honesty, it will take you a couple of hours of work to complete this self-study guide. You may have to dust off a few junior high school algebra lessons. The gestalt-switch, thought-conversion geometry causes may take months to process, but the time and effort will be well spent. What you will learn will invite a lifetime of contemplation.

I welcome questions, suggestions, and dialogue. I wish you continuous success as you apply designed experiments to improve patient safety and the quality of care. And as we all know by now, as the quality of care improves the costs of human suffering shrink.

M. Daniel Sloan
Sloan1@ix.netcom.com

Acknowledgments

Full credit for the design of experiments quality improvement tool goes to Pythagoras, René Descartes, Sir Ronald Fisher, and George E. P. Box. There is nothing in this book that has not already been implied, explained, or illustrated in their work. This little guide tries to make the poetry of Fisher and Box easier to appreciate. I hope playfulness adds simplicity to their work.

Pythagoras, the first true mathematician, proved that for a right triangle where c is the hypotenuse, $c^2 = a^2 + b^2$. Evidently, around 1912 Fisher noticed that the algebraic expression for the sum of the squares in the analysis of variance was a synonym for Pythagoras's theorem. See Figure A.1. Fisher's genius level insight adds a refreshing degree of clarity for all of us who struggled through our statistics class in college wondering what in the world "sum of the squares" meant.

Box, a Fellow of the Royal Society and a Shewhart Medal winner from ASQC, fleshed out the details and drew the essential pictures of Fisher's model with J. Stuart Hunter and William G. Hunter in their masterpiece, *Statistics for Experimenters: An Introduction to Design, Data Analysis and Model Building*.

All of this information surfaced and became clear during a series of clinical quality improvement projects at Highline Community Hospital in Seattle, Washington. Cheryl Payseno, Helena Villablanca, Linda Paulson, Loretta Edwards, Annette Milanowski, Marge Carlson, Dave Brumfield, Laura McHenry, and a dozen other nurses applied theory. They produced results—knowledge and insight. They also proved designed experiments are powerful. Designed experiments can help improve patient safety and improve the quality of care.

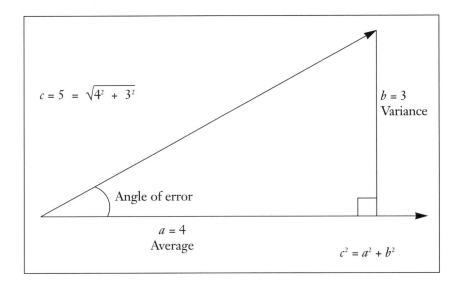

Figure A.1. The length of the observation vector *c* (any series of counts or measures) equals the square root of the sum of its squared elements, *a* and *b*. The model can be extended to any number of dimensions, as will be shown in Table 5.8 (page 107). The right triangle in this Pythagorean triple [3, 4, 5] graphs two observations in two dimensions (4, 3). For reference *a* and *b* could be relabeled $x = 4$ and $y = 3$. The average *a* represents the idealized perfect model. The variance *b* is the difference between the ideal model and actual observations. In medicine, Pythagoras's theorem, $c^2 = a^2 + b^2$, is sometimes referred to as Einthoven's law of electrocardiography, lead II = lead I + lead III.

The Center for Quality and Productivity Improvement at the University of Wisconsin in Madison provides an extraordinary five-day learning experience in designed experimentation. Box, Dr. Søren Bisgaard, and Dr. Conrad Fung are three of the world's best quality science educators. They have developed an efficient and effective sequential learning process. I believe their teaching sequence is critically important to understanding the designed experiments model. Their sequence inspired the teaching sequence in this guide.

My tutor and proofreader, Dr. Stephen Jones, a graduate of the University of Wisconsin-Madison and a statistician at the Boeing Company, patiently shared his expert knowledge. Stephen explained quality in 24 dimensions, the experimental cube, half-normal probability plots, Pythagoras's theorem, residuals, design resolution, how to handle missing values, and the sum of the squares with good humor. Thank you, Stephen. You are a world-class educator.

When Betty Gwaltney, RN, a colleague in Anchorage, Alaska, showed me Frank Netter's classic illustration of Einthoven's orthogonal planes,[1] the locked box of continuous, clinical health care improvement popped open. Replace the three-dimensional sphere on the cover of this book with a heart, and you will see what we saw. Geometry is beautiful in any dimension. Betty's imagination, intelligence, personal industry, study habits, and applications of theory typify the best that health care professionals have to offer their patients.

Finally, thanks go to my wife, Lynne, and my son, Austin. Over the past eight years science, math, and statistics have become favored toys in our family. Austin and I constructed 16 helicopters together. While I cross-checked and reworked experimental results I thought were incorrect, Austin redesigned our product and doubled our helicopters' flight times just by looking at the pictures. This is a very important lesson for any adult who doubts the power of designed experimentation. After a day of fly fishing in the North Fork of the Snoqualmie River, he built the experimental cubes and tetrahedrons of a three-factor interaction so that I could understand them. Austin's aim with a catapult is impeccable. His sky divers are fearless. Lynne's background laughter is inspirational music to my ears. Their love enriches my life beyond measure.

Section I

Practical Applications: Using Designed Experiments to Improve Health Care Quality and Shrink Health Care Costs

UNIT ONE

Directed Experimentation

Medicine is a science about which we know very little, in relationship to a patient about which we know even less, for which we prescribe treatments about which we know absolutely nothing.

—John Striebel

LEARNING OBJECTIVES

1. Students will be able to identify and explain at least four benefits of disciplined discovery and efficient learning.
2. Students will be aware of the leadership contributions made by Ronald A. Fisher, Walter A. Shewhart, W. Edwards Deming, and George E. P. Box.
3. Students will be able to identify theoretical, philosophical, and practical differences and similarities between statistical method from the viewpoint of quality control and the design of experiments.

THE OBLIGATIONS OF A WELL-EDUCATED PERSON

The scientific method proposed by Francis Bacon in 1605 has produced a wealth of knowledge. Bacon's notions about efficient learning, experimental observation, and the accurate recording of experimental data are as old as Aristotle and as fresh as a new idea.

Knowledge produced in the twentieth century redefines the phrase *well-educated person*. Studying the design of experiments (DoE) is a remarkable way to learn how much of your college course work holds up to the test of time. As we approach the twenty-first century, the phrase *well-educated person* means that a person uses the language of science, statistical reasoning, on a daily basis. Personal computers make this competency standard a reasonable expectation for elementary students as well as veteran corporate executives.

Well-educated people know how to interpret experimental evidence, statistics. They expect those statistics to be graphed in a meaningful way. Quality-literate people understand and apply the sound, circular logic of inductive and deductive reasoning. Educators who championed this logic include Aristotle, Galileo, Immanuel Kant, Albert Einstein, Ronald A. Fisher, Walter A. Shewhart, and W. Edwards Deming. Every adult who serves in a leadership position has an obligation to role-model the behaviors of a well-educated person, including the use of statistical reasoning.

The obligation for health care organizational leaders is clear: replace high-risk guesswork and gambles with well-reasoned decisions. Patient safety always comes first. When patient safety comes first, the quality of care improves and the total costs of delivering health care diminish.[1] The total costs of care include emotional and human, financial, and economic losses.

SHRINKING THE COST OF POOR-QUALITY HEALTH CARE JUDGMENTS

Poorly reasoned health care judgments cost lives, jobs, and billions in wasted dollars. One need only look as far as a bar graph for evidence to support this thesis. A bar graph is an enumerative and descriptive picture. Bar graphs provide no ground for a well-reasoned decision whatsoever. Yet bar graphs are the favored analytic tool for many bureaucratic health care clinical, financial, and operational judgments. Judgment quality guides decisions. Decision quality drives costs.

Bar graphs promote poor-quality judgment. They square the costs of lazy logic. The erroneous, four-year cost accounting trend analysis, included in the final success stories unit of this book, expands on this theme. Lucky, good-guess diagnostic related group (DRG) examples (see Figures 1.1 and 1.2) are included here for quick illustration.

A well-managed DRG 210, a hip pinning, can earn a provider $8,786 in reimbursement. Poorly managed, a DRG 210 can produce significant losses. Health care management teams often use bar graphs to show that different outcomes are produced by different providers.

Figure 1.1 may be used to support the position that this difference is statistically significant.

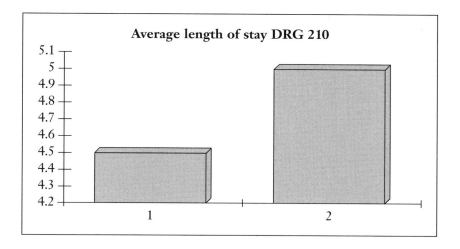

Figure 1.1. Provider 1 had a 4.5 average length of stay. Provider 2 had a 5-day length of stay.

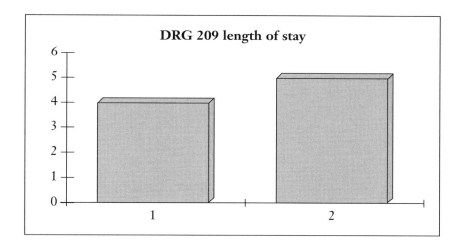

Figure 1.2. Provider 1 has a lower average length of stay than provider 2 for DRG 209.

DRG 209, hip and knee replacements, can earn a provider $11,049. In a typical health care organization, Figures 1.1 and 1.2 are all the evidence needed to support the judgment that provider 1 does a significantly better job of management than provider 2. No one asks about the median, mode, measures of dispersion, probability, reliability, or other qualities that create profit or loss.

Bureaucrats often use complementary bar graphs to justify, among other things, managed care contracts. Everyday bureaucrats wager people's jobs on the basis of a cavalier hunch. Sometimes they are lucky, sometimes not. Fifty–fifty guesswork is a bad business practice.

Sad to say, but from 1985 to 1990, when I worked as a regional medical center vice president, I ignorantly nodded my head in enthusiastic agreement when this brand of sophistry passed for analysis. Sophistry is plausible but fallacious argumentation. If there were an easier way to own up to this error, I would take it, but there is no other way to say it.

Regrettably, I confess to endorsing needlessly risky, oftentimes terrible, executive decisions, *poor-quality decisions*, that were made to spend millions and millions of dollars on the strength of misleading bar charts. Awakening to the realization of one's responsibility for squandered resources is traumatic.

After studying the work of Shewhart and Deming, I have worked to end this kind of nonsensical reasoning. In the course of my work as an educator and consultant, I am meeting an increasing number of leaders who are waking up to honesty's alarm clock. Many are deciding the time is right and that they have just enough personal power to dramatically change things for the better.

Unfortunately, I still see people lose their jobs because they can't "produce these kinds of numbers." I have seen dozens of hospitals close as a direct result of bar graph sophistry. I watch as others prepare to close. Other than the fact that bar charts are easy to draw, I am baffled as to why bar charts enjoy such favor.

The correct analytic computation process for deciding whether the difference between two means is significant is an analysis of variance, called ANOVA. (ANOVA calculations are detailed in unit 4.) With a few clicks of a computer button and about 10 seconds of time, a spreadsheet application calculates and explains that there is no statistical difference between the means for DRG 210. The difference between the means for DRG 209 is statistically significant. The spreadsheet application output for these two analyses is detailed in Tables 1.1 and 1.2.

Table 1.1. No significant difference between the means. Statistical significance most definitely is not a synonym for practical significance. Note the F value, 0.875821. This is the quotient produced from dividing the mean square (MS) between groups by the MS within groups. Fisher created a table of F critical values that is now automatically calculated for us with software.

ANOVA: Single-Factor		DRG 210		
Summary				
Groups	Count	Sum	Average	Variance
Provider 1	13	59	4.538462	2.102564
Provider 2	32	163	5.09375	3.700605
Source of variation				
	SS	*df*	MS	F	P value
Between groups	2.850481	1	2.850481	0.875821	0.354575
Within groups	139.9495	43	3.25464		
				F crit	
Total	142.8	44		**4.067047**	

Table 1.2. A significant difference between the means, under the assumption that the two population variances are not significantly different. ANOVA significance does not suggest predictability or reliability. An F test statistic describes neither the variance nor the pattern of variation around the mean over time.

ANOVA: Single-Factor		DRG 209		
Summary				
Groups	Count	Sum	Average	Variance
Provider 1	71	302	4.253521	1.877666
Provider 2	29	153	5.275862	3.064039
Source of variation				
	SS	*df*	MS	F	P value
Between groups	21.52028	1	21.52028	**9.708557**	0.002406
Within groups	217.2297	98	2.21663		
				F crit	
Total	238.75	99		**3.938112**	

The ANOVA F test statistic, the ratio of two estimated variances, helps us determine whether differences between several group means are significant or not. The F test was named in honor of Fisher, a twentieth-century statistical genius who created DoE. In the DRG 210 example, the F value (0.875821) is less than the F critical value (4.06704). The one-way ANOVA indicates that there is no significant difference between the two population means. For DRG 209, the F test statistic shows that there is a statistical difference.

As helpful as an ANOVA is in the context of designed experimentation, a single statistic doesn't tell us enough. How reliable has the process been? Export the data to a statistical process control application and, in a few seconds, we have a much improved understanding.[2] See Figures 1.3–1.6. The difference in the means for DRG 209 is not statistically significant, but the patterns of variation for both of provider 1's DRGs in comparison to provider 2 are of immense economic significance. We can make sound judgments, which lead to higher-quality decisions, improved quality, lower costs, and profitability. Think it through.

The deductive bureaucratic analysis is inadequate for well-reasoned and responsible decisions. Bar graph logic is not true. It cannot build trust or confidence. Correctly guessed answers nurture doubt. Habitual guessing and the inevitable doubts created by guesses raise costs.

The graphic language of applied science, statistical analysis, provides the truest picture of what is really happening in this economic and clinical system. The honest language of inductive reasoning—counting, measuring, and drawing statistical pictures—builds trust, faith, and respect. Inductive reasoning provides the best picture of what is happening and what can happen.

There is no comparison. Bar graph gambling is ruinously expensive. Honest, inductive analytic reasoning and meaningful graphic summaries are a bargain. The scientific method can help us lower costs. Imagine the possibilities!

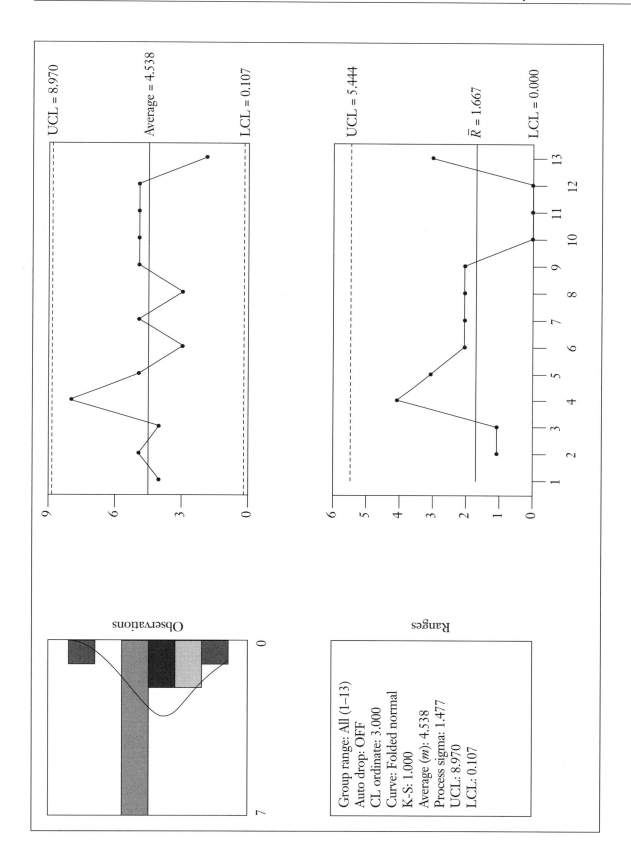

Figure 1.3. Provider 1—DRG 210 mean and variability are detailed.

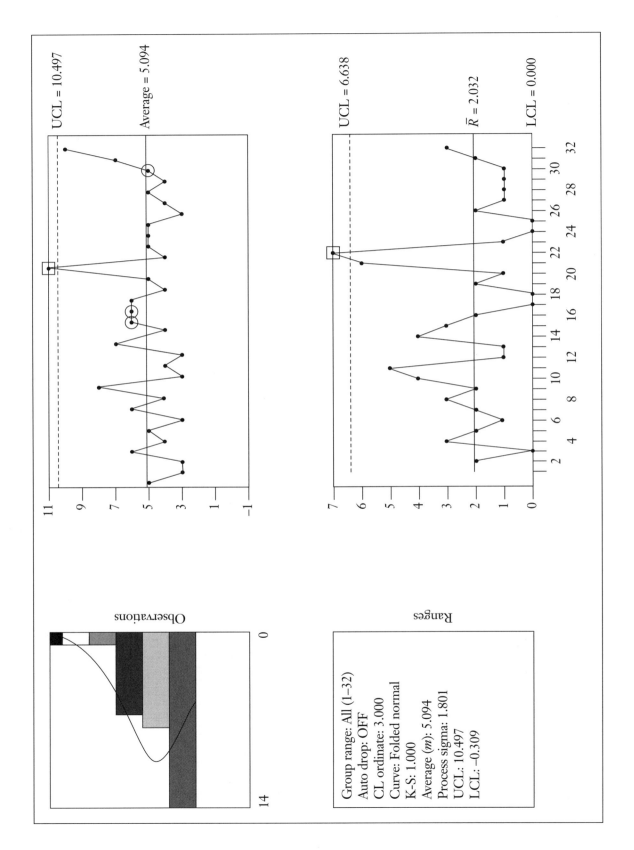

Figure 1.4. Provider 2—DRG 210 mean and variability are detailed. Special cause, improbable variations are marked with circles and squares.

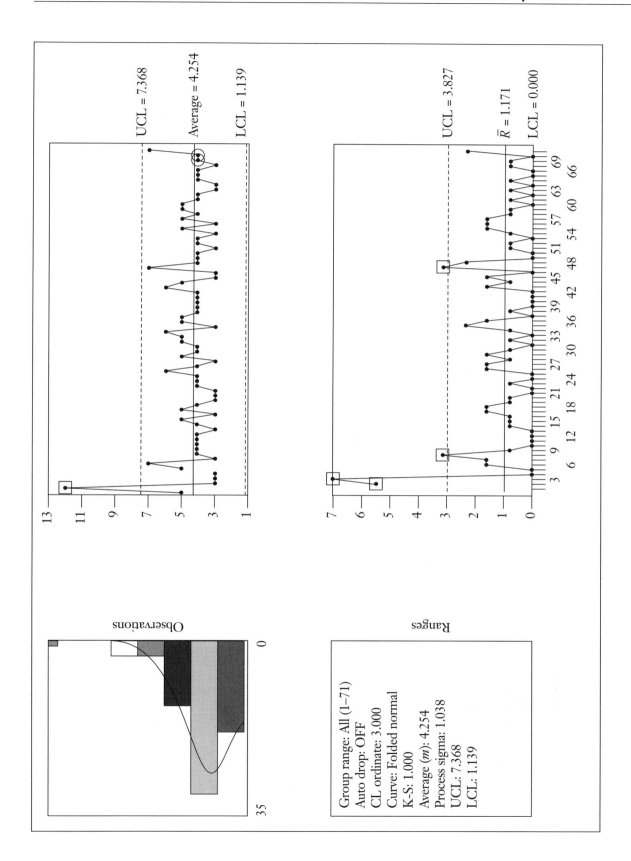

Figure 1.5. Provider 1—DRG 209 mean and variability are detailed. Special cause, improbable variations are marked with circles and squares.

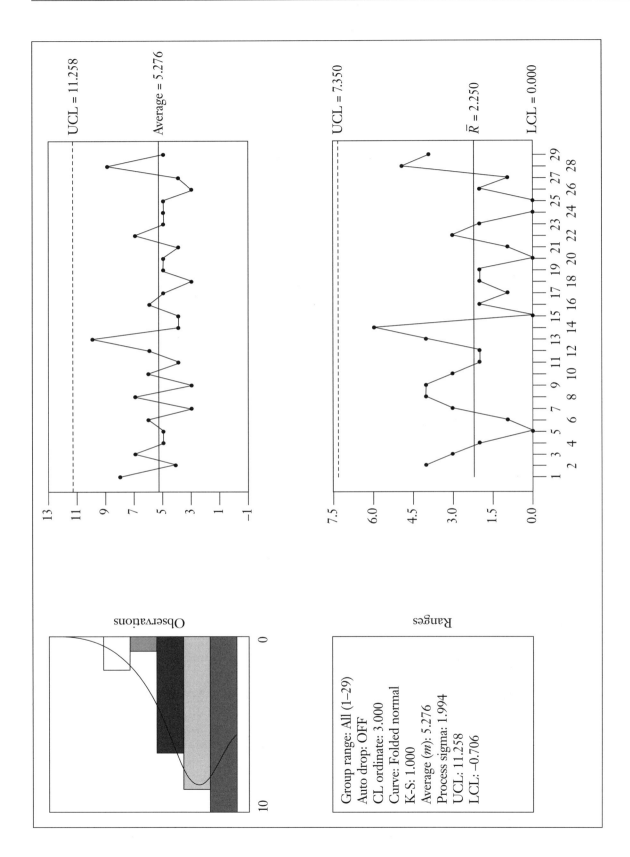

Figure 1.6. Provider 2—DRG 209 mean and variability are detailed.

BENEFITS OF DISCIPLINED DISCOVERY AND EFFICIENT LEARNING IN THE HEALTH SCIENCES

Disciplined discovery, applied science's method, rewards us with knowledge and prosperity.

1. The scientific method and statistical reasoning teach us lessons about qualities, quantities, perception, variability, and variation.

2. Disciplined observation and statistical investigation can help us gain an understanding about which main factors and which factor interactions affect the outcome of any given process. This knowledge can help us improve the quality of our lives.

Experimentation, observation measurements, and well-reasoned analysis are universal, knowledge-discovery tools. Varying the factors in any process constitutes an experiment. Combined variables, in the context of an experiment, are called *experimental treatments*. Different treatments mean different combinations. Experimental treatments are used in all professions to find out what works best. *Treatment* is a word with a rich tradition in agriculture, medicine, and statistics. The geometrical, statistical methods of designed experiments expose factor interactions, linear relationships, and nonlinear relationships. Computers let people of all ages graph these relationships in meaningful ways.

Treatment variations found in day-to-day, medical science applications are immense. The infinite amount of variability, known and unknown, found in any biological system of any size adds to this complexity. The geometry of designed experiments introduces simplicity to our lives.

With science and statistics we can investigate and systematically learn how these main-factor and interaction effects cause patient outcomes. Science and statistical investigation can help us understand the physical mechanisms of a process. We can begin to understand why factors in a given treatment behave the way they do. The geometry of designed experiments allows us to visualize and quantify these factors in any number of dimensions.[3]

As we enter the twenty-first century, two analytic tool sets, (1) statistical method from the viewpoint of quality control and (2) directed experimentation, are indispensable to the health sciences. Although this book is about designed experimentation, quality control charts abound. Each tool set interprets qualities of variation. Interpretations are predictions. Predictions invite control. As our predictions and control improve, we can continuously improve future patient outcomes.

The benefits of disciplined discovery and efficient learning to the health sciences include, but are not limited to, the following:

Benefit 1: Directed experimentation is economical!
The results designed experiments produce, the counts and measures we record while observing a process, help us efficiently discover what works. It takes less than 15 minutes for the average adult or child to learn how to apply the fundamentals of a designed experiment.

Statistics for Experimenters: An Introduction to Design, Data Analysis, and Model Building by Box, Hunter, and Hunter provides sound theory for making the scientific method affordable.[4] Computers and software make science practical. Directed experimentation, DoE, is less expensive than trial and error.

Sound theory—systematically organized knowledge that is applicable in a wide variety of circumstances—allows us to analyze, predict, or otherwise explain the nature or behavior of a specified set of phenomenon. DoE systematically organizes knowledge quickly and inexpensively. Directed experimentation helps us efficiently answer the question, "What do we need to do to produce the outcome we want?"

Fisher took experimentation out of the laboratory and literally put it into the field.[5] Microsoft's *Encarta* program tells us,

> Fisher was a British mathematician, whose statistical theories made scientific experimentation far more precise. Fisher showed that by partitioning the variations of a body of data, one can accurately assess how they influence one another and the outcome of the experiment. Used first in biology, his statistical designs quickly became

influential and were applied in agricultural, medical, and industrial experimentation.[6]

Fisher's original idea, the application of n-dimensional Euclidean space for experimental designs, has proven to be highly successful. Studies in mathematics and theoretical physics at Cambridge from 1909 to 1912 eventually led to a lifetime of pioneering work. Fisher's ideas on genetics sowed the seeds of biometric genetics. His keen interest in human genetics led to research work in human blood groups and the clarification of the inheritance of the Rhesus groups.[7]

Personal computers and software applications give every person the opportunity to put Fisher's ideas to work on their desktop. People of all ages can enter their experimental results and produce a sophisticated statistical analysis in minutes.

Box, Hunter, and Hunter comment on the importance of plotting data in the age of computers.

> Without computers, most of the work done on non-linear models would not be feasible. . . . The computer is fast and precise; the human mind is comparatively slow and inaccurate. But whereas the mind's power of critical and inductive reasoning are very great, those of the computer are minuscule.[8]

The quality of health care depends on the thoughtfulness of the intervention process. The combination of people, sound science applications, and computing technology creates an opportunity for economical isomorphism, an information-preserving transformation.[9] In simple language, this means everybody and anybody at any age can benefit from the scientific method. Statistical analysis is as simple as counting, measuring, and drawing pictures.

Benefit 2: Factorial and fractional factorial experimental designs let us study multifactor interactions simultaneously. The investigation dogma that a proper experiment should be conducted one factor at a time, in a controlled environment, can be put to rest.

Many, if not most, people who attended school from 1940 to 1996 learned that only one experimental factor can be varied and studied at a time. Two serious problems plague this approach. First, the expenditure of time and money required to run one-factor-at-a-time studies render this brand of experimentation prohibitively expensive. Second, one-factor-at-a-time studies never reveal interactions. Statistical significance produced in a controlled study is rarely a synonym for practical significance.

Fisher demonstrated that vectors and the coordinate geometry associated with the analysis of a sample can provide insight into the nature of statistical procedures such as the t test and analysis of variance.[10] Fisher illustrated that Pythagoras's theorem and the ANOVA equation are identical algebraic statements.

In effect, the quality of a given measurement, taken at any moment in the continuous passage of space and time, can be represented in three dimensions. See Figure 1.7. The statistical cube used to describe quality in this book can be extended to any number of dimensions.

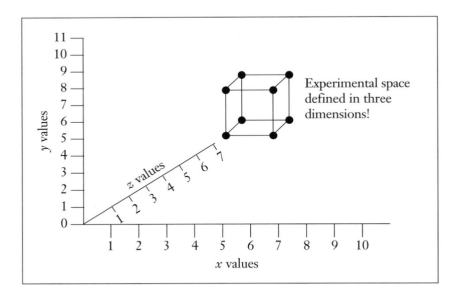

Figure 1.7. Shewhart included this illustration in *Economic Control of Quality of Manufactured Product* in 1931. Deming drew a similar picture in *Some Theory of Sampling*. The Fisher/Box notion of sequential continuous discovery in *n* dimensions echoes Einstein's principle: The evolution of an empirical science is a continuous process of induction through space and time.

Box simplified and systematically extended Fisher's work. Box's ideas on modeling strategy, response surface methodology, and statistical inference can be credited with bringing the idea of directed experimentation into everyday life.

> **Benefit 3: Speed. Directed experimentation quickly produces high-quality solutions to important puzzles!** Designed experiments are the most efficient way to learn how to improve a process.

Sixty years ago, factorial and fractional experimental designs were quickly put to use in agriculture to increase crop yield. Since crops grow slowly and harvest comes but once a year, one-factor-at-a-time experimentation was and remains impractical. During the 1930s and 1940s, a time of crisis in U.S. agricultural and military history, directed experimentation promoted the rapid discovery of factors that produced higher quality and larger quantities of products. Historical connections between the quality sciences, the creation of the Bell telephone system, farming production increases during the 1930s, medical science advances in the 1940s, and the Allied victory in World War II are strong.

Deming, a quality sciences champion of international reputation, entered the U.S. Department of Agriculture on August 1, 1927.[11] As one of his activities, Deming invited "great men to give lectures." Fisher was one of his guests. In 1938, Deming invited his colleague and friend Shewhart to give what became a seminal series of lectures. Shewhart's presentations were published as *Statistical Method from the Viewpoint of Quality Control.*[12]

Prior to the 1938 lectures, Deming recalled that Shewhart fretted over the clarity of his writing. "He [Shewhart] said that his writing had to be fool-proof. I thereupon let go the comment that he had written his thoughts so damn fool-proof that no one could understand them." Deming's observation was and remains prophetic.

World War II created a sense of urgency for mastering the art of finding fast and reliable solutions to complicated, life-threatening puzzles. Statistical method from the viewpoint of quality control provided puzzle solutions. Reliable communication systems, ammunition, and ordnance were three noteworthy contributions. According to Box's firsthand report as a statistician in the British Army during the war, efficient statistical and mathematical investigations played important roles in the air defense of England.

In the United States, Shewhart, Deming, George W. Edwards and other experts in statistical reasoning provided guidance throughout the war.[13] The Statistical Research Group, Applied Mathematics Panel, Office of Scientific Research and Development, organized in July 1942, assisted the Navy, Army, and the Office of Scientific Research.[14]

War accelerated the process of discovery that Thomas Kuhn described as "extraordinarily arduous." In *The Structure of Scientific Revolutions* Kuhn commented, "Normal science, for example, often suppresses fundamental novelties because they are necessarily subversive of its basic commitments."[15]

The need for an Allied victory over the Nazi and Axis forces gave novel ideas that worked priority over theoretical and less practical ideas that had enjoyed favor in less dangerous times. Breakthroughs occurred in agriculture, armaments, and the health sciences. The need to provide higher quality health care services at a continuously reduced cost creates a similar opportunity. Novel ideas that work are now being tested and implemented.

The maturation of the scientific method, the advent of statistical tools, personal computers, and the development of a global communication system that disseminates information have contributed to rapid technological growth.

Figure 1.8 is an intuitive summary that isolates the evolution of medical treatment effectiveness. Effectiveness is a dimension of quality known as reliability. Penicillin, the Salk vaccine, laser surgery, and magnetic resonance imaging have proven themselves to be effective technologies. New and less expensive strategies—prevention, quality controlled medical records, patient- and caregiver-designed experiments—and less expensive technologies—outpatient surgery and medication—are now threatening to make old technologies like inpatient surgery look primitive.

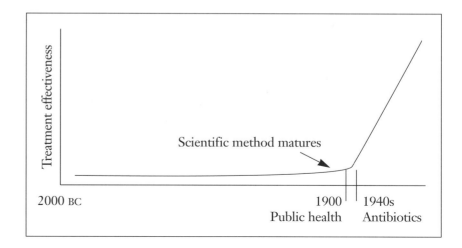

Figure 1.8. Medical science timeline. The twentieth century has witnessed the advent of effective public health measures, medicines, and technology.

Benefit 4: Measurement and analysis, an essence of true science and honest statistical investigation, provide a structure for ethical, rational, well-educated, and profitable decisions. The knowledge that an education affords an individual creates an ethical imperative. Well-educated people have an obligation to use their knowledge for the common good. Quality decisions often lead to prosperity.

"The dream of reason did not take power into account." With this sentence, Paul Starr began his Pulitzer prize–winning book, *The Social Transformation of American Medicine*.[16] A literate and statistically numerate workforce equipped with personal computers necessarily alters the structure of power and authority in the health care industry. Knowledgeable individuals increasingly decline opportunities to surrender their private judgment to bureaucratic authority.

Since power abhors competition as nature abhors a vacuum, reaping the benefit of ethical and rational decisions creates an exciting challenge. I believe most health care leaders are willing to meet this challenge with honesty and integrity. Patient safety really does come before personal profit for most caregivers. I see evidence of this every day in my work.

THE INTELLECTUAL ADVENTURE

The power of the health sciences, results-based quality improvement, and personal computing emerges when well-educated individuals grasp the significance of difference, sameness, and abstraction. This awareness leads to a recognition of paradox and the profound ambiguity that is the world around us.

The paradoxical differences between statistical method from the viewpoint of quality control and directed experimentation link them together in a profoundly meaningful abstract concept, *quality*. The methods are one and the same. As Shewhart suggested, our current knowledge of the nature of light provides an apt statistical metaphor. See Figure 1.9.

Sir Isaac Newton's theory of light described its quality as an emission of particles. Christiaan Huygens's theory was that the quality known as light travels by a wave motion. Quantum theory holds that these two apparently mutually exclusive and conflicting theories are complementary. Quantum theory has shown that in some experiments light acts like a series of particles and in

Figure 1.9. A high-quality crystal can break white light into a full spectrum. Cinematographers know how only three colors—blue (*x*), red (*y*), and green (*z*)—can be combined to produce moving rainbows.

other experiments it acts like a wave. Quality acts like a series of numbers, a cube, a sphere, a wave, and a smile.

Differences

The significant differences that exist between an analysis completed with the tools of directed experimentation and statistical process quality control are theoretical, philosophical, and practical.

Theoretical Differences: When Box is asked about the importance of a process's state of statistical control, he replies, "I do not believe there is any such thing." Statistical method from the viewpoint of quality control requires a definition of the statistical state of control prior to taking action on a process.

Philosophical Differences: Statistical method from the viewpoint of quality control holds that one must first reason by abandoning the a priori. This position is a central tenet in conceptual pragmatism and C. I. Lewis's theory of knowledge.[17] The quality scientist must reason without the bias of prior assumption or prior knowledge. Observations must be free from the bias that prior knowledge creates.

DoE requires the quality scientist to start with a set of theoretical a priori assumptions, geometry. Geometry and astronomy defined the word *revolution* for science. In effect, DoE leverages one's knowledge bias with a revolutionary reference frame. Designed experiments apply the prior knowledge an informed observer has concerning a process.

With DoE, it is implicitly understood that an informed observer has an advanced working knowledge of algebra, geometry, and statistical reasoning. Informed observers have ready access to advanced personal computing technology. Since the results of any experiment can only be as good as the experimental assumptions, the scientist is honor bound to relentlessly question and test every assumption.

Democracy, social activism, and political activism are explicitly a part of statistical method from the viewpoint of quality control. Although chapter 3 of *Statistics for Experimenters* is entitled, "Random Sampling and the Declaration of Independence," with the design of experiments, agendas for social improvement play a secondary role to scientific investigation.

Practical Differences: The standard statistical process quality control chart and its companion, the two-dimensional scatter diagram, describe the world in two dimensions. As inadequate as this reference frame is for describing the world as we know it, people of all ages and educational backgrounds can quickly learn to understand what the pictures mean. The pictures, quality control charts, help people produce results.

Directed experimentation describes the world in multi-dimensional terms.

Box, Hunter, and Hunter graciously acknowledge that "it is not easy to imagine a space of more than three dimensions."[18] Nonetheless, the directed experimentation model, Fisher's model, describes and predicts a given quality in any number of dimensions. For good measure and to demonstrate their point, they cite an example with 24 dimensions and illustrate response surfaces with many more.

Informed observers are expected to take the time required to look at the world in this fashion. Given the power of personal computers, this is a perfectly reasonable expectation.

Similarities

The beauty and artistry of designed experimentation and statistical process control contain identical elements. Just as combinations of primary colors—red, blue, and yellow—will produce millions of different print colors, three universal measurement and analysis categories can produce an infinite number of shades, hues, and levels of understanding. The unifying elements of analysis, the sameness of directed experimentation and statistical process control, are theoretical, philosophical, and practical.

Box speaks eloquently for both approaches when he says, "Birds gotta fly. Fish gotta swim. People gotta be creative." The heavy role that imagination, intuition, and deduction play in the process of disciplined discovery is as Einstein described it to be in 1917 when he commented, "Imagination is more important than knowledge."[19]

Theoretical Similarities: Genius-level philosophers and scientists agree. Aristotle, Galileo, Bacon, Descartes, Hume, Kant, Einstein, Fisher, Shewhart, Deming, and Box suggest that we reason inductively first. Induction improves the quality of deduction. Since David Hume's work, *An Inquiry into Human Understanding,*[20] the sequential order data, the succession of perceptions, has been known to contain the information needed to increase knowledge and improve processes. In our work, we call this process the IDEA cycle: *i*nduction, *d*eduction, *e*valuation, and *a*ction.[21]

Both approaches to quality improvement, DoE and statistical process control (SPC), wisely mistrust sacred assumptions of random sampling. Both techniques fully appreciate the fact that the passage of time alters process. Constantly changing qualities, variations, in people, materials, methods, machinery, the environment, and measurements soon invalidate the hypothesis of random sampling.

Deming's $k_1 k_2$ inspection rule articulates an economic incentive for doubting a hypothesis of randomness. In their comments on the hypothesis of randomness, Box, Hunter, and Hunter observe, "For real data the property can never be relied on, although special precautions in the design of an experiment can make the assumption relevant."[22]

SPC requires the scientist to sequentially plot counts or measures of a single quality. Reasoning without the bias of prior knowledge can help us discover quality breakthroughs. The universal standards for measurement and analysis are identical to all scientific investigations (see Figure 1.10). Categorical and allegorical thinking transfers this knowledge across the borders of all professions.[23]

The process of plotting data sequentially over time without a preconceived notion about what is to be observed is level-one induction.[24] Control charts provide an important fundamental tool to the mastery of first-degree inductive reasoning. Each dot plotted on a chart represents one complete cycle of the scientific method: hypothesis, experiment, test hypothesis.

Fisher and Box argue for a wider inductive basis. With authority, they suggest that by observing the important effects of factors in an experiment under a variety of conditions, the

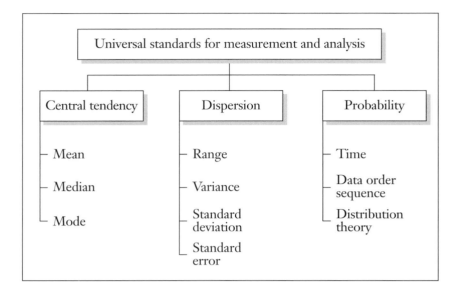

Figure 1.10. Thoughtful, well-reasoned, and logical analysis is central to all professional work. All health care professionals must discipline themselves to the daily application of these statistical reasoning elements for all clinical, operational, and financial processes.

inferences produced by the experiment are more likely to be true in general. Quadratic algebraic expressions and geometry provide theory for a wider inductive basis.[25] Fisher's geometrical description of the analysis of variance provides the shoulders for Box to stand on. Geometry makes the analysis process robust.[26]

Box added the all important sequencing of experiments to continuously produce knowledge. His proposal, evolutionary operation, could have been taken from the first paragraph of Einstein's book, *Relativity*.

> The author [Einstein] has spared himself no pains in his endeavor to present the main ideas in the simplest and most intelligible form, and on the whole, in the sequence and connection in which they actually originated.[27]

Box's model generates a continuous series of new hypotheses. In the process of producing more questions than answers, it creates remarkable insight.

This book strives to emulate this sequential learning process so that students can experience the discovery process for themselves.

Philosophical Similarities: Both approaches, SPC and DoE, follow the principles of classical Greek thought. The Shewhart/ Deming cycle follows Aristotle's inductive, circular logic. Box cites Sophocles.

Statistical method from the viewpoint of quality control was heavily influenced by Lewis's philosophy, conceptual pragmatism.[28] (A thorough literature search reveals Aristotle's *Posterior Analytics* and *Eudemian Ethics* as the origin of this philosophy.) Shewhart and Deming's emphasis on producing a good social order is more explicit than Box's proposals for scientific investigation.

Fisher and Box's use of geometry is the obvious link to Greek classical thinking. Though it is presented more subtly, philosophy plays a crucial, subtle role in directed experimentation. One cannot hope to understand the implications of Box's model without studying experimental philosophy.

Practical Similarities: Both tool sets are pragmatic; *do what works!* This pragmatic bias is a principle in solution-focused, results-based quality improvement. Since life's complexity is mysterious beyond our understanding, to a certain extent we must rely on empirical observation. Both approaches are deeply concerned with economy and practicality.

Deming dogmatically prescribed that no one should take action on any process before establishing its statistical state of control. To do so, according to Deming, was tampering. Tampering, as demonstrated by the Monte Carlo funnel experiment, increases variation.[29] Increased variation erodes the quality dimension of reliability.

Box cites the second law of thermodynamics as evidence that there is chaos, not statistical control. He suggests that since some, if not all, processes can never be brought into control, one would never be able to run an experiment at all. Box recommends interference. He prescribes tampering. From Box's viewpoint, directed experimentation increases the probability of an informative event occurring.[30] Informative events lead to improvement.

Physics rises to the challenge of transforming this superficial paradox into a similarity. Close observation of both tool sets (SPC and DoE) in action reveals that at the high, abstract, and conceptual level, these conflicting investigative approaches are indistinguishable. They reflect each other.

The Unifying Link

To observe a process is to change a process. As every quality improvement scientist has seen in actual practice, to measure a process is to change a process!

By observing a process, Deming tampered with every process he observed. He observed for positive effect. Box openly acknowledges that experimentation is tampering: quadratically and geometrically. He recommends that we observe for positive effect. Observation and tampering by an informed observer—directed experimentation—creates a positive effect with either method.

First-data illustrations in the work of Shewhart, Deming, and Box describe the passage of time. The sequential order of data is of paramount importance to the art and science of discovery. In all three models, perceptions of successive events are enhanced by counting, measuring, and drawing a picture. This graphic, inductive, analytic process is the essence of the IDEA cycle and solution-focused quality improvement. See Figure 1.11.

- Solution-focused, results-based quality improvement suggests that people use statistical analysis to quickly eliminate undesirable process variations.

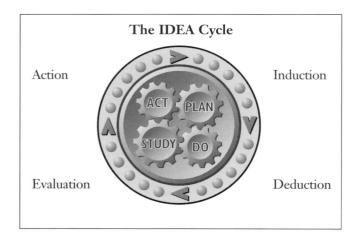

Figure 1.11. The IDEA cycle creates rapid quality improvements while it shrinks costs.

- Solution-focused, results-based quality improvement suggests that people use statistical analysis to systematically replicate desirable process variations.

To listen to these educators, from Aristotle to Box, is to hear an egalitarian message of democratic principle and intellectual liberty. People at all levels of society can benefit from economical applications of the scientific method. All people should have access to an education that makes discovery affordable.

The motto for both models is, "Do what works!" Do more of what works to improve the quality of life. SPC and DoE are two tool sets that make the discovery process delightfully productive.

UNIT TWO

Gestalting Quality: The Fast Track to Shrinking Health Care Costs

It is indifferent for our illustration for what purpose the mixture may be required. It may be an industrial product, a medicinal prescription, or an artificial manure.

—Sir Ronald Fisher

LEARNING OBJECTIVES

1. Students will be able to define vocabulary words in the design of experiments including *gestalt, algebra, quadratic, vector, abscissa, ordinate,* and *orthogonal.*

2. Students will be able to describe a strategic questioning process and explain why strategic questioning is an efficient way to converge on the truth.

3. Students will have a useful metaphor for graphically illustrating the parallel between experimentation in the life sciences and the physical sciences.

4. Students will be able to demonstrate an aerobic exercise experiment, a parachute experiment, and a catapult experiment to show how the method of designed experiments works.

IMPORTANT VOCABULARY WORDS

A *gestalt* is a physical, biological, psychological, or symbolic configuration or pattern of elements so unified as a whole that its properties cannot be derived from a simple summation of its parts.[1] A given quality cannot be adequately described in mechanistic terms. One must consider the quality's system in all of its dimensions. Three-dimensional vectors and geometric, graphical representation permit us to consider a quality in all of its complexities.

The vocabulary of designed experimentation is important to using DoE successfully. The following definitions are key.

Algebra is a generalization of arithmetic in which symbols, usually letters of the alphabet, represent numbers or members of a specified set of numbers and are related by operations (addition, substitution, transposition, and so on) that hold for all numbers of that set.[2] All algebraic expressions can be represented graphically with geometry. For example, the algebraic expression, $a + 2$, represents a straight line a plus its two points. Draw a straight line with a point at each end to illustrate this equation for yourself.

A *quadratic equation* has one or more of the terms squared, but raised to no higher power. The general form of a quadratic equation is $ax^2 + bx + c = 0$ where a, b, and c are constants.[3] The algebraic expression for a square, a *quadratic expression*, is $(a + 2)^2$. $(a + 2)^2 = a^2 + 4a + 4$. a^2 is the plane of the square. $4a$ represents the four lines. Plus there are four corner points in a square. Draw a square with a point at each corner to illustrate this equation. Label each of the four lines a.

Cubic and higher-order equations. The algebraic expression for a cube is $(a + 2)^3$. The formula $(a + 2)^3 = a^3 + 6a^2 + 12a + 8$. a^3 is the cube's surface. $6a^2$ represents the six planes. $12a$ represents the cube's 12 edges. Plus there are eight corner points in a cube. Draw a three-dimensional cube to illustrate this equation.

The general form for a cube in n dimensions is $(a + 2)^n$.

A *vector* is a quantity that is completely specified by magnitude and direction. A line with an arrow is often used as the graphic description of a vector. The length of a vector is the square root of the sum of the squares of its elements. Two vectors are summed by summing corresponding elements.[4] The length of data vector y [2, 5, 3] $= \sqrt{4 + 25 + 9}$.

An *abscissa*, symbol x in mathematics, is the coordinate representing the position of a point along a line perpendicular to the y axis in a plane Cartesian coordinate system. (See Figure 2.1.) Cartesian mathematics is named for Descartes, who not only introduced analytic geometry and algebraic solutions to geometric problems, he pioneered the use of exponents.

An *ordinate*, symbol y in mathematics, is the Cartesian coordinate representing the distance from a specified point to the x axis, measured parallel to the y axis.

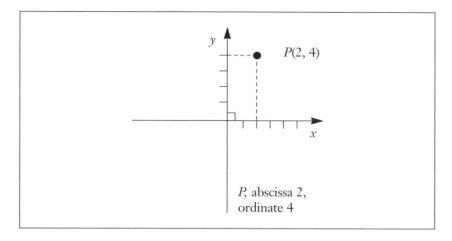

Figure 2.1. *P* represents a quality as a functional relationship between one *x* and one *y* value.

Orthogonal. When two vectors come together at a 90° angle, the vectors are said to be orthogonal. The ordinate and abscissa in a Cartesian coordinate system are orthogonal. A vector can be drawn from *y* to *x* thus forming a right triangle. In the context of designed experiments, orthogonality allows us to estimate the average effects of experimental factors without worrying that results are being distorted by other factors.[5] In a two-level orthogonal array, each factor level can be coded as a +1 or –1. (In a table of trigonometric functions, when the angle is 90°, the sine equals 1.0000 and the cosine equals .0000.) When one multiplies the row values from each column in an experimental array and adds up the products, the sum will be equal to zero. Table 2.1 illustrates this key concept for creating experimental arrays.

Directed experimentation applies this quadratic and geometrical knowledge base to create breakthrough improvements. Two elements are essential to success with the design of experiments.

EXPERT KNOWLEDGE AND STRATEGIC QUESTIONING

First, expert subject matter knowledge and intellect are main ingredients for success. The expert must have a working knowledge of elementary algebra and geometry, statistical method, and the process under investigation in order to form well-educated opinions. A well-educated hypothesis is more valuable than an

Table 2.1. Sound geometry creates a sound analysis of variance. Orthogonality is essential to both concepts.

Main factor	$B_1 - 1$	$B_2 + 1$
$A_1 - 1$	1. $A_1 - 1$ $B_1 - 1$	3. $A_1 - 1$ $B_2 + 1$
$A_2 + 1$	2. $A_2 + 1$ $B_1 - 1$	4. $A_2 + 1$ $B_2 + 1$
Experimental array—example of orthogonality				
Randomized order of experiments	Standard order	Factor A	Factor B	Row products $A \times B$
4	1	−1	−1	+1
1	2	+1	−1	−1
3	3	−1	+1	−1
2	4	+1	+1	+1
		Sum = 0	Sum = 0	Sum = 0

uneducated hypothesis. Professional experience, intuition, and the imagination provided by intellect can and often do lead to high-quality deductive inferences.

There also must be a rational and economical investigation strategy for posing and answering questions. The game 20 Questions illustrates the strategy perfectly. Through a systematic, this/that process of dividing an experimental space into continuously diminishingly sized halves, this game leads to a convergence on the truth.[6] Any number of halve-paths can lead to the solution. For example, suppose the object, or quality, to be guessed is Eric Clapton's guitar. Players must have expert subject matter knowledge. They need to know who Eric Clapton is and what a guitar is if they have any hope of uncovering the solution.

Question	**Answer**
1. Is the object associated with humans?	Yes
2. Is it male or female?	Male
3. Is it famous or not?	Famous
4. Is it connected with the arts?	Yes
5. Is it music or a painting?	Music

Question	Answer
6. Is it from this century or not?	This century
7. Is it rock and roll or classical music?	Rock
8. Is it an instrument or a piece of music?	An instrument
9. Is the object Eric Clapton's guitar?	Yes

Figure 2.2 illustrates an efficient yes/no strategy of halves with lines, vectors, right angles, and squares. As the experimental space of the strategic questioning shrinks, experimenters can converge on the truth. The universal system of measurement and analysis (see Figure 1.10 on page 24) combines with statistical method from the viewpoint of quality control and directed experimentation to create rapid breakthroughs in quality.

The expert knowledge afforded by a professional education and license places caregivers in the dominant leadership role for quality improvement. Experienced caregivers are the best source of informed observers for a given clinical process. Since caregiver judgments drive all economic decisions in the system, improving these judgments takes top priority. High-quality decisions, decisions that improve quality, lower the total costs related to providing health care to the patient.

Experimental space

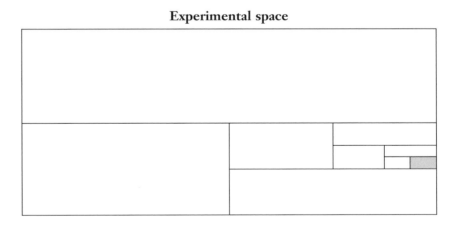

Figure 2.2. The expense of trial-and-error guesswork is systematically reduced by a strategic questioning process. Note the plane geometry and orthogonality of the process.

Figures 2.3–2.6 illustrate several familiar clinical measures. Control charts, scatter diagrams, and designed experiment graphs are absolutely appropriate clinical decision support tools. One can argue persuasively that there is an ethical imperative to use these tools on a case-by-case, diagnosis-by-diagnosis, treatment-by-treatment basis. In fact, Sir Austin Bradford Hill (1897–1991), a leader in the application of statistics to medical research, did precisely that.

> The medical profession has a responsibility not only for the cure of the sick and for the prevention of disease but for the advancement of knowledge upon which both depend. This third responsibility can be met only by investigation and experimentation.[7]

Hill, Fisher, Box, and other thought leaders in the field are leaders because they developed a talent for seeing categorical similarities over the chaos and complexity that marks minute differences in instance. Great leaders must be great teachers. Fisher and Box, in particular, not only taught, they wrote superb textbooks so the rest of us could learn the value of their wisdom.

Every day that I have gone to work for the last nine years, someone shares an observation with me that runs along these lines. "Well, I can see how your example applies to a CAT scan analysis, but I don't see its relevance for an MRI analysis." Or, "I can see how your control chart may have relevance for graphing pCO_2 measurements, but it seems a bit contrived to use the same chart for graphing O_2 measurements." Or, "I can see how one might use a designed experiment in an aircraft manufacturing process, but I can't imagine how it would work in a patient care process."

The tip-off phrase for difficult communication is, "I can't imagine." Some people do not imagine adventuresome ideas, concepts, or categories. To be sure, this shortcoming is not a comment on their worth as individuals. They just have a tough time imagining. Leaders must teach and show these people how to imagine and how to think categorically. Leaders must teach by example. Shewhart, Deming, Fisher, and Box are role-model teachers for promoting high-quality imagination and creativity.

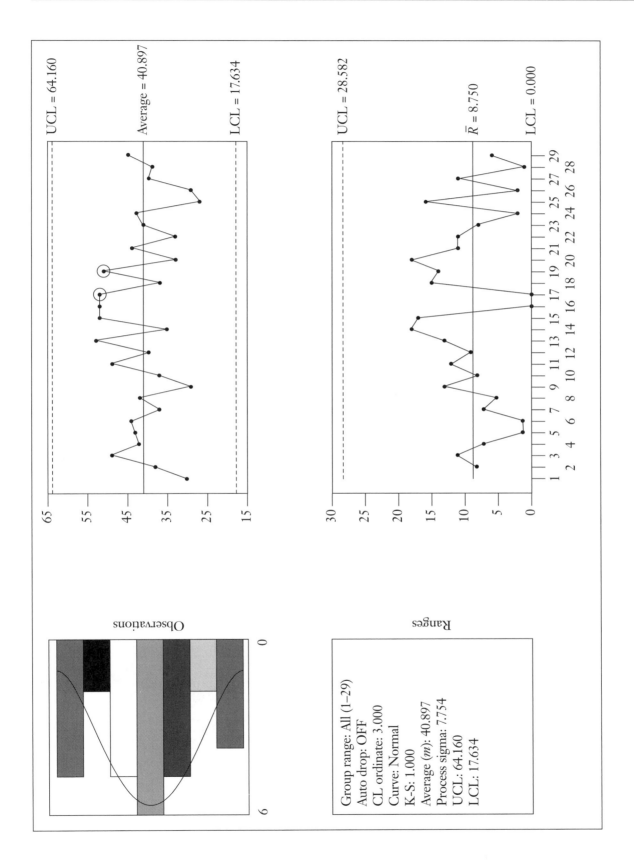

Figure 2.3. pCO₂ blood gases process.

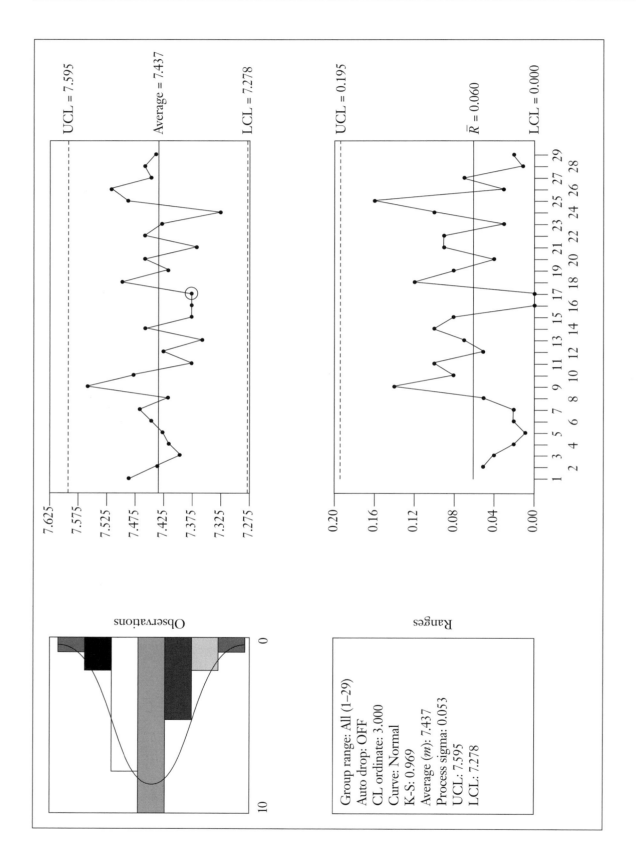

Figure 2.4. pH blood gases process.

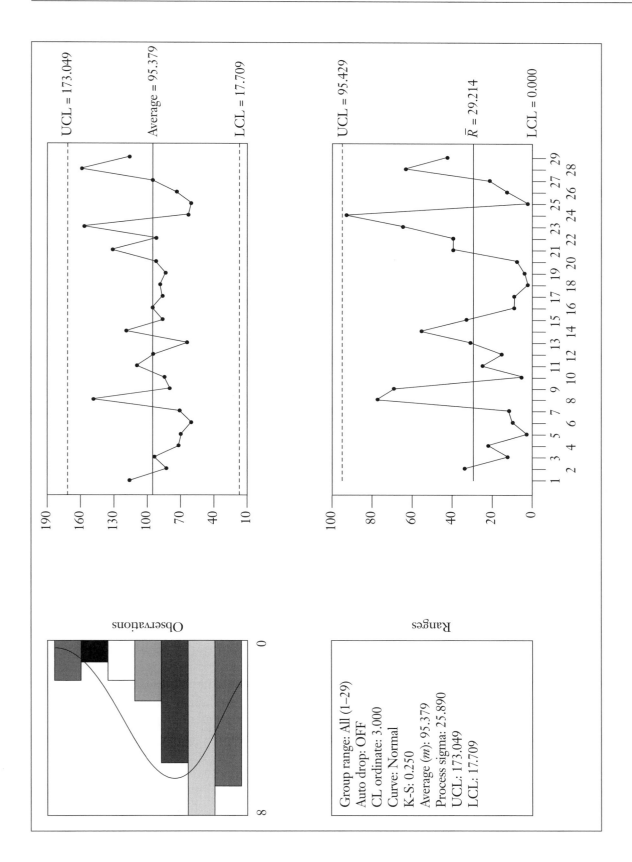

Figure 2.5. O$_2$ blood gases process.

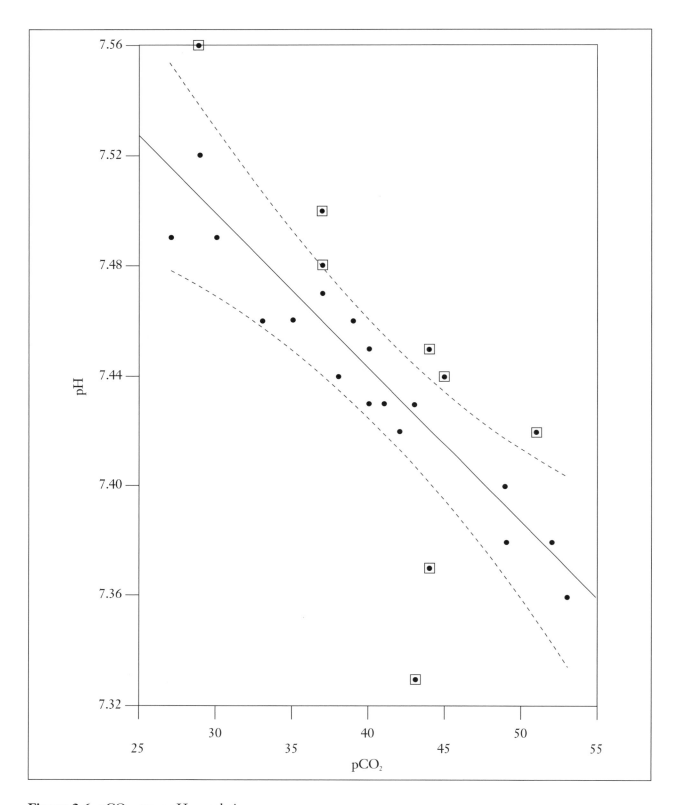

Figure 2.6. pCO$_2$ versus pH correlation.

The words *analysis*, *measurement*, *cost*, and *process* establish categories. A variable is a variable is a variable. Context creates important differences, but the language of science, the principles of statistical reasoning, and the scientific method are universals that go across all borders of knowledge and knowing.

Incredibly, there is still widespread reluctance by nurses and physicians to use the quality control statistical tool set to improve patient safety. "We've never done it that way before," is the usual explanation, forgetting for the moment that every time they read an EKG they do exactly that. As solution-focused, results-based quality improvement continues to produce significant results, change is coming. Affordable computers, Internet connections, clinical statistical process control, and designed experiments are making the predictions in *The Quality Revolution and Health Care* come to life.[8]

Fisher wrote about the importance of categorical thinking to the design of experiments. He knew 60 years ago, as Shewhart knew, that these methods had universal applications.

> The knowledge which guides us in increasing the precision of an experiment is not a knowledge of the individual peculiarities of particular experimental units, such as plots of land, experimental animals, coco-nut palms, or hospital patients, but a knowledge that there is less variation within certain aggregates of these than there is among different individuals belonging to different aggregates.[9]

Figures 2.7–2.23 summarize common ground between control chart and design of experiments sampling plans. Recall that the *I* in the IDEA cycle suggests that the first two pictures drawn using observation data are a control chart and a scatter diagram, complete with a regression analysis.

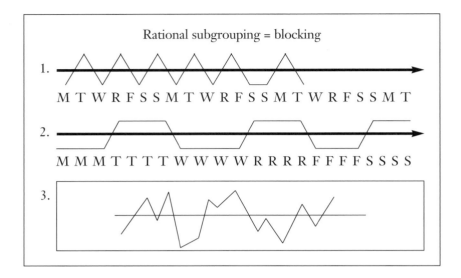

Figure 2.7. Imagine that these three patterns chart three different sampling plans. The *x* axis graphs the passage of time. The up-and-down patterns graphed along the *y* axis document variable observation values. Data collection sequence and data presentation can lead to different inductive inferences. Three different subgroups are illustrated here. Block (rationally subgroup) what you can and randomize what you cannot is a rule to follow with the use of directed experimentation. Subgroup homogeneity is more important than the number of experimental replications.

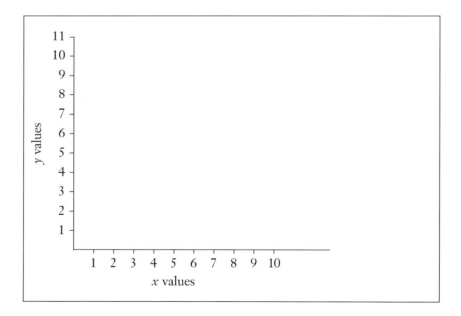

Figure 2.8. The ordinate and abscissa are the original frame for DoE.

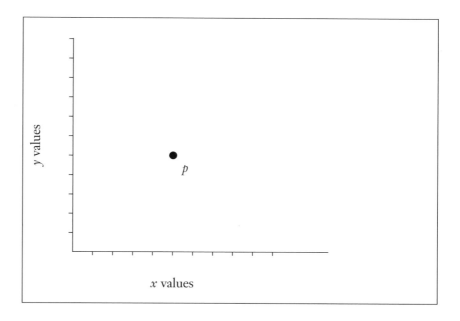

Figure 2.9. A data point p is identified in two dimensions. p is a function of x and y.

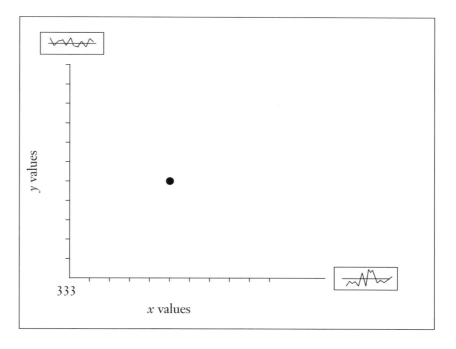

Figure 2.10. It is implicitly understood that the data point comes from two distributions taken in sequential order through time. Control charts are ideal for observing and understanding quality in two dimensions.

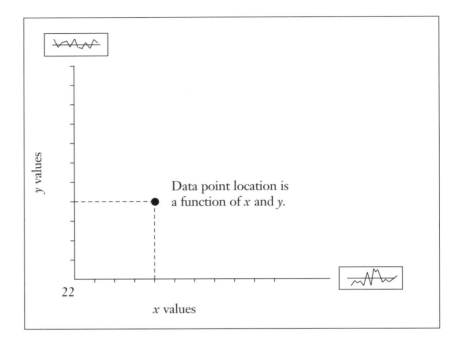

Figure 2.11. Inductive analytic reasoning establishes a two-dimensional, experimental space.

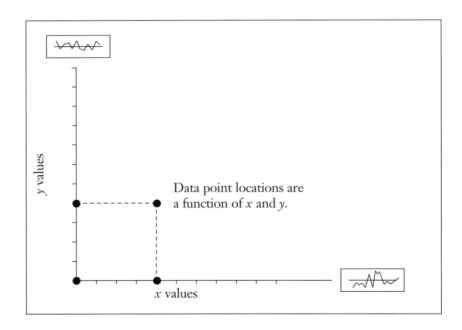

Figure 2.12. The first strategic question square is identified for analysis.

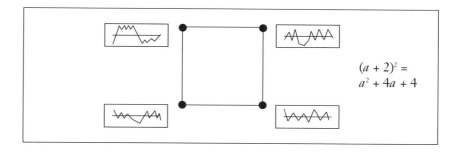

Figure 2.13. The strategic question square can be placed anywhere in space and time, $(a + 2)^2$.

Note: The wider inductive basis, literally and figuratively, for experimentation has been established. Inductive, analytic reasoning, a method of thought in which a conclusion is reached about all members of a set by examining just a few members of the set, is key to high-quality thinking. High-quality thinking and accurate, precise inferences can help you produce high-quality results. As thought quality improves, the costs of trial-and-error failure diminish in health care just as they do in all other industries, corporate or personal.

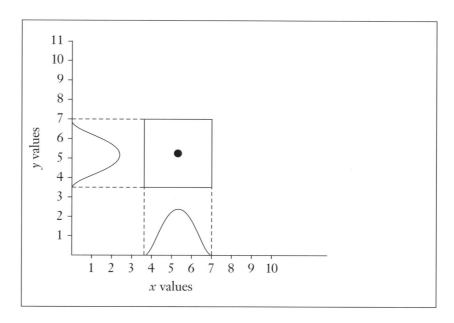

Figure 2.14. An experimental space can be drawn around the data point so that the two distributions are implicitly represented.

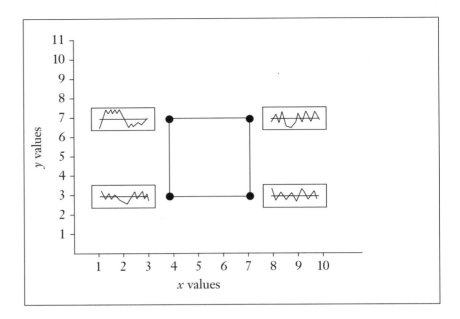

Figure 2.15. Measurements taken at each corner of the box will vary over time. The average of a rational subgroup of four creates a screening frame for statistical inference.

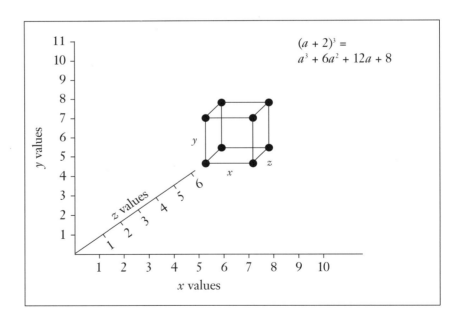

Figure 2.16. Three values can be represented simultaneously and geometrically. Note the square, orthogonal, 90° right angle arrangement of the vectors. Note the planes of the cube, $(a + 2)^3$.

Figure 2.17. Square, orthogonal plots of land have been used in agriculture for centuries. The quincunx planting pattern for fruit trees creates a two-dimensional area of opportunity for sampling. A quincunx is an arrangement of five objects, one at each corner of a square or rectangle, with one in the middle.

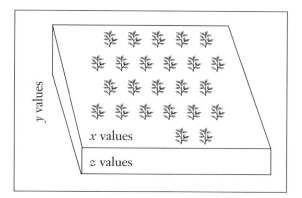

Figure 2.18. Yield has as much to do with soil temperature (z) as it does with the width (x) and length (y) of a given field.

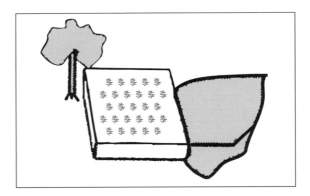

Figure 2.19. External environmental factors affect the sample area. Water can seep through the soil. A tree gives shade, which affects temperature. Falling leaves affect the nitrogen content of the soil.

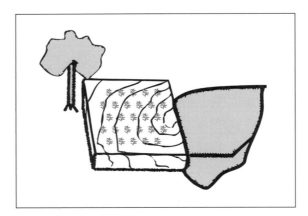

Figure 2.20. Different agricultural soil treatments produce different levels of fertility and yield. This three-dimensional topographical map of soil quality, *x*, *y*, and *z*, can be extended to any number of dimensions.

Figure 2.21. Layers of soil illustrate some of the variables related to fertility and growth. Two-dimensional illustrations lack the richness required for a more complete understanding.

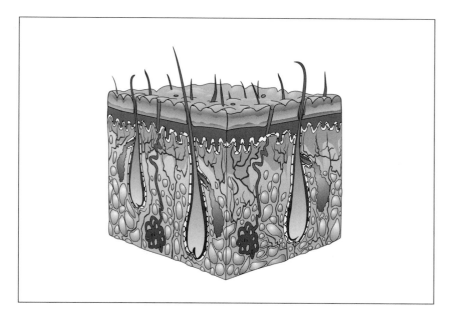

Figure 2.22. Epidermal agriculture! Imagination and categorical and allegorical thinking lets us see a striking graphic parallel between the life sciences and the physical sciences. Width *x*, length *y*, and depth *z* are universal measurements.

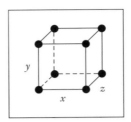

Figure 2.23. This experimental space can be constructed around any quality in any context. Algebra and geometry improve the inferences we deduce from our counts and measures. This cube is the gestalt switch of the health sciences quality revolution. A gestalt switch causes people to abandon less rewarding paradigms.

The decision to sample a process quality must be based on a rational and logical hypothesis. The rational subgroup from statistical process control is called a *block* in DoE. A rational sample is one that is taken in a timely manner with sensible and sound reasoning. Rational samples are homogenous. The more representative and homogenous a sample is, the more reliable the inferences you make become. In the design of experiments, homogeneous samples are a key to continuous success.

Randomizing the sampling process minimizes the bias that occurs during any observation process. The experimenter who bases judgments on a rational hypothesis, a rational block, and a randomized sampling plan will experience more success than one who omits these logical disciplines.

For example, dermatitis is sometimes diagnosed by taking a sample of skin from patient A. The skin sample location affects deductions made from the sample. The width (x), length (y), and depth (z) of the skin sample will also affect deductions. (It would be irrational to use patient A's sample to diagnose patient B's skin problem.) Moisture, nutrients like nitrogen and oxygen, and temperature affect the growth of fruit trees as well as the growth of hair.

Diabetic patients provide another excellent reference analogy for arraying the variables related to blood glucose. As with all high-quality medical care, diabetic regimes are individualized. Currently, trial-and-error experimentation is the norm for establishing and adjusting the best combinations of weight, height, activity levels, insulin administration, complex and simple carbohydrate intake, fat intake, and protein intake. With designed experiments, these factors (x, y, z) can be combined to consistently produce the best outcome.

Directed experimentation can and does improve the quality of inferences made without the benefit of calculation, data plotting, and a formal analysis. Few health care professionals argue against this principle. Personal computers and DoE software make this kind of analysis fast and affordable. The time has come for all health care professionals to act on their principles every time they make a clinical decision.

FAST-TRACK EXPERIMENTS

Welcome to world of fast-track improvement. The destructive myth that health care quality improvement takes years to produce results is finally and completely discredited. In the next 15 minutes you will have a template tool that you can immediately use to improve health care quality and shrink costs. Quality Health Systems of America, Inc., happily grants you permission to freely copy and use the blank template.

The experimental cube can be easily constructed using an intermediate set of K'NEX® construction toys.* Check your child's toy closet. There may already be a cube you can use to orient yourself. If you don't have an outfitted toy closet, use Figure 2.24.

Figure 2.24. An orthogonal experimental array model for easy reference.

---

*Quality Health Systems of America, Inc. gratefully acknowledges K'NEX® Industries, Inc., for permission to use its name and toys to illustrate the experimental cube.

Note the x axis is the *abscissa* and the y axis is the *ordinate*. Imagine that the z axis goes off into space. Each corner of the cube represents a different combination, also called a *permutation*, of the eight possible combinations of the three factors (x, y, and z) set at two levels each. In DoE language this is a 2^3 full-factorial experiment.

The corners are labeled 1–8. Each number corresponds to an experimental run. By running the eight experimental runs, you will be able to intuitively analyze the experimental results. When you run an ANOVA study, a regression analysis, and 12 statistical charts on the DoE software program you are going to buy, you will find that the math supports what you learned just by looking at the numbers on the cube. Now examine the completed experiment template in Figure 2.25.

To save time, please don't ask questions! We've only got another 12 minutes to go. Observe that all of the large values fall on the back plane, which is defined by the cube corners 5, 6, 7, and 8. Note that the two highest values fall on points 7 and 8.

The measured experimental response is heart rate. The three factors we are investigating are x (male or female), y (no weight or yes weight in a backpack), and z (resting position and running in place). Yes, you could substitute respiration rate for heart rate. But this is a race against the clock. Run your own experiment later.

Run number 1, point number 1 on the lower left, front face of the cube is the heart rate of a man, who was not wearing a backpack and who was sitting down. His resting heart rate was 72. Run number 2, point number 2 on the cube, is the heart rate of a woman who was not wearing a backpack and who was sitting down. Her resting heart rate was 68. The other points follow the orthogonal array.

Quality Science Questions: Based on the eight data points, what inferences can you make? Of the three factor settings in the experiment, which one caused a high heart rate? What two-factor interaction produced the highest heart rates? Based on the results of the study, do you think gender makes a difference in heart rate?

Factors ☞ Runs ▼	x sex	y weight	z exercise	Response heart rate
1	−1 = male	−1 = no	−1 = no	72
2	+1 = female	−1 = no	−1 = no	68
3	−1 = male	+1 = yes	−1 = no	80
4	+1 = female	+1 = yes	−1 = no	76
5	−1 = male	−1 = no	+1 = yes	140
6	+1 = female	−1 = no	+1 = yes	136
7	−1 = male	+1 = yes	+1 = yes	156
8	+1 = female	+1 = yes	+1 = yes	160
Sum	0	0	0	

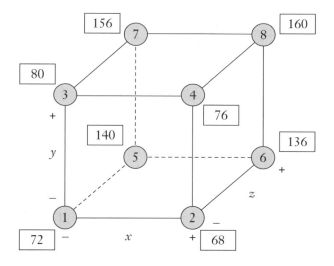

Effects formula: Add four points on a given plane and divide by four. Add four points on the opposite plane and divide by four. Subtract low settings, coded with a minus sign, from high settings, coded with a plus sign. Effect magnitude estimate equals the difference between averages.

$$x = \frac{2+4+6+8}{4} - \frac{1+3+5+7}{4}$$

$$\text{Sex} = x = -2$$

$$y = \frac{3+4+7+8}{4} - \frac{1+2+5+6}{4}$$

$$\text{Weight} = y = 14$$

$$z = \frac{5+6+7+8}{4} - \frac{1+2+3+4}{4}$$

$$\text{Exercise} = z = 74$$

Place each measured response in the appropriate box. Do the values suggest a wider inductive basis for improvement action? Why or why not?

Figure 2.25. Completed 2^3 worksheet.

Quality Science Answers: The difference between the averages of the opposing planes estimate the effect of the factor. Aerobic exercise is a main factor with an estimated effect value of 74. The weight of the backpack is also a main factor, with a value of 14. Relatively speaking, gender does not affect heart rate. When exercise is also a weight-bearing event, heart rates increase. This is a universal two-factor interaction!

By now, you have been staring at the cube long enough that it has inverted. In other words, the back plane has become the front plane and you are looking at it from underneath instead of the topside down. This metaphor, DoE turns the world of data upside down, is but one discovery you will make with designed experiments. Incidentally, Nobel laureate Francis Crick uses this optical illusion to explain how our brain works in his book *The Astonishing Hypothesis.*[10]

Now find three companions and replicate the experiment using the blank template in Figure 2.26. It takes five minutes. Replication is the essence of science. Yes, designed experiments really are easy. Many times you can tell just by looking at the cube what is going on in a process or system.

Let's apply what you know using another household toy, a catapult. If you don't have a catapult, you may want to buy one of those too. They are a wonderful teaching tool and a hoot to play with. A Lightening Calculator model is shown in the Figure 2.27.[11] The stuffed bear adds a touch of realism. Health care professionals who served in any artillery division in the armed forces may find themselves commenting, "We used vectors, measurements, and analyses like these all the time to sight targets."

The three variables are *x* (fixed vertical arm height, low or high), *y* (trigger height, low or high) and ammo (yellow or painted). Distance is the quality we are interested in. (See Tables 2.2 and 2.3.)

Examine the distance in inches on the template in Figure 2.28. Can you tell just by looking at the array and the cube what the important factors and the two-factor interactions are? Big numbers mean the shot went far. Small numbers mean it didn't go so far. What is fascinating is that the mathematics, algebra, and geometry of the design will support your intuition.

Factors ☞ Runs ▼	x		y		z		Response measure
1	−1 =		−1 =		−1 =		
2	+1 =		−1 =		−1 =		
3	−1 =		+1 =		−1 =		
4	+1 =		+1 =		−1 =		
5	−1 =		−1 =		+1 =		
6	+1 =		−1 =		+1 =		
7	−1 =		+1 =		+1 =		
8	+1 =		+1 =		+1 =		
Sum	0		0		0		

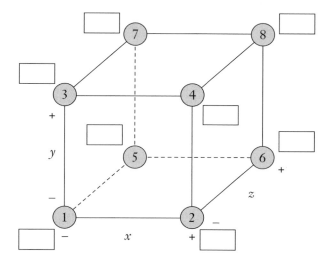

Place each measured response in the appropriate box. Do the values suggest a wider inductive basis for improvement action? Why or why not?

Effects formula: Add four points on a given plane and divide by four. Add four points on the opposite plane and divide by four. Subtract low settings, coded with a minus sign, from high settings, coded with a plus sign. Effect magnitude estimate equals the difference between averages.

$$x = \frac{2+4+6+8}{4} - \frac{1+3+5+7}{4}$$

$$x =$$

$$y = \frac{3+4+7+8}{4} - \frac{1+2+5+6}{4}$$

$$y =$$

$$z = \frac{5+6+7+8}{4} - \frac{1+2+3+4}{4}$$

$$z =$$

Two-factor interaction planes:

$$x \times z = \frac{1+3+6+8}{4} - \frac{2+4+5+7}{4}$$

$$x \times y = \frac{1+4+5+8}{4} - \frac{2+3+6+7}{4}$$

$$y \times z = \frac{1+2+7+8}{4} - \frac{3+4+5+6}{4}$$

Three-factor interaction tetrahedron:

$$x \times y \times z = \frac{3+8+2+5}{4} - \frac{4+7+1+6}{4}$$

Figure 2.26. Blank 2^3 worksheet. You may want to program a spreadsheet application to replicate this template. This will speed and simplify these calculations.

Figure 2.27. Catapult practice is fun for everyone.

Table 2.2. Computer-generated orthogonal array with definitions of variables.

Label	Type	Levels	
Fixed arm	Main factor	2	Qualitative
	Low 2″		
	High 5″		
Ammo	Main factor	2	Qualitative
	Painted 5″		
	Yellow 5.5″		
Trigger height	Main factor	2	Qualitative
	Low 1.5″		
	High 4″		
Distance	Response		

Table 2.3. Computer-generated analysis array and interaction array codes. The pictures produced from this series of experiments are shown in Figures 2.29–2.36.

Orthogonal analysis array			
Fixed arm	Ammo	Trigger height	Distance
Low	Painted	Low	58″
Low	Painted	High	48″
Low	Yellow	Low	59″
Low	Yellow	High	52″
High	Painted	Low	105″
High	Painted	High	79″
High	Yellow	Low	106″
High	Yellow	High	77″

We're done with the first two fast-track experiments and there is time to spare! How would you set the variables for maximum distance? How would you set the variables for short distances?

Here is a health care improvement hint: Doesn't length remind you of length of stays, short and long? How about days in accounts receivable, short and long? Now you have a tool to help you figure out what causes what. Your tool will help you solve clinical, operational, and financial process puzzles.

Factors ☞ Runs ▼	*x* *Fixed arm*	*y* *Trigger*	*z* *Ammo*	Response measure
1	−1 = *Low*	−1 = *Low*	−1 = *Yellow*	67″
2	+1 = *High*	−1 = *Low*	−1 = *Yellow*	111″
3	−1 = *Low*	+1 = *High*	−1 = *Yellow*	51″
4	+1 = *High*	+1 = *High*	−1 = *Yellow*	80″
5	−1 = *Low*	−1 = *Low*	+1 = *Painted*	65″
6	+1 = *High*	−1 = *Low*	+1 = *Painted*	104″
7	−1 = *Low*	+1 = *High*	+1 = *Painted*	48″
8	+1 = *High*	+1 = *High*	+1 = *Painted*	79″
Sum	0	0	0	

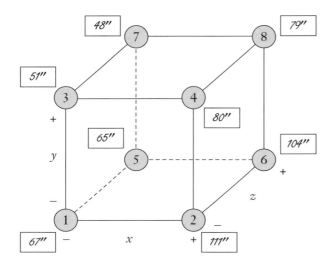

Place each measured response in the appropriate box. Do the values suggest a wider inductive basis for improvement action? Why or why not?

Effects formula: Add four points on a given plane and divide by four. Add four points on the opposite plane and divide by four. Subtract low settings, coded with a minus sign, from high settings, coded with a plus sign. Effect magnitude estimate equals the difference between averages.

$$x = \frac{2 + 4 + 6 + 8}{4} - \frac{1 + 3 + 5 + 7}{4}$$

$$x =$$

$$y = \frac{3 + 4 + 7 + 8}{4} - \frac{1 + 2 + 5 + 6}{4}$$

$$y =$$

$$z = \frac{5 + 6 + 7 + 8}{4} - \frac{1 + 2 + 3 + 4}{4}$$

$$z =$$

Figure 2.28. 2^3 worksheet for continuous improvement.

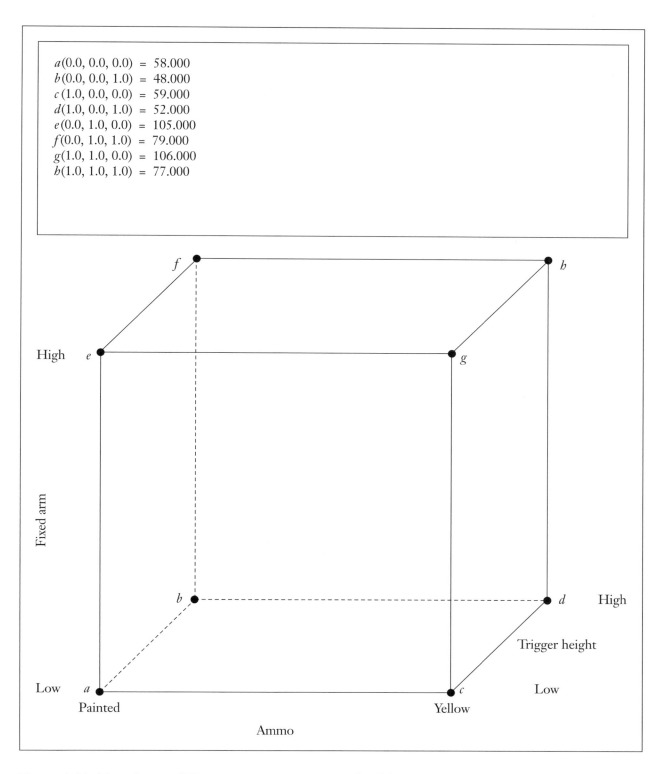

$a(0.0, 0.0, 0.0) = 58.000$
$b(0.0, 0.0, 1.0) = 48.000$
$c(1.0, 0.0, 0.0) = 59.000$
$d(1.0, 0.0, 1.0) = 52.000$
$e(0.0, 1.0, 0.0) = 105.000$
$f(0.0, 1.0, 1.0) = 79.000$
$g(1.0, 1.0, 0.0) = 106.000$
$h(1.0, 1.0, 1.0) = 77.000$

Figure 2.29. Note that two different experiments were completed for our catapult study. We replicated the experiment to confirm our results. The computer-generated array (Table 2.3 on page 55), response values, and graphic configuration of the computer analysis differ from the template shown in Figure 2.28. Which factor still stands out? Which plane contains all long-distance values?

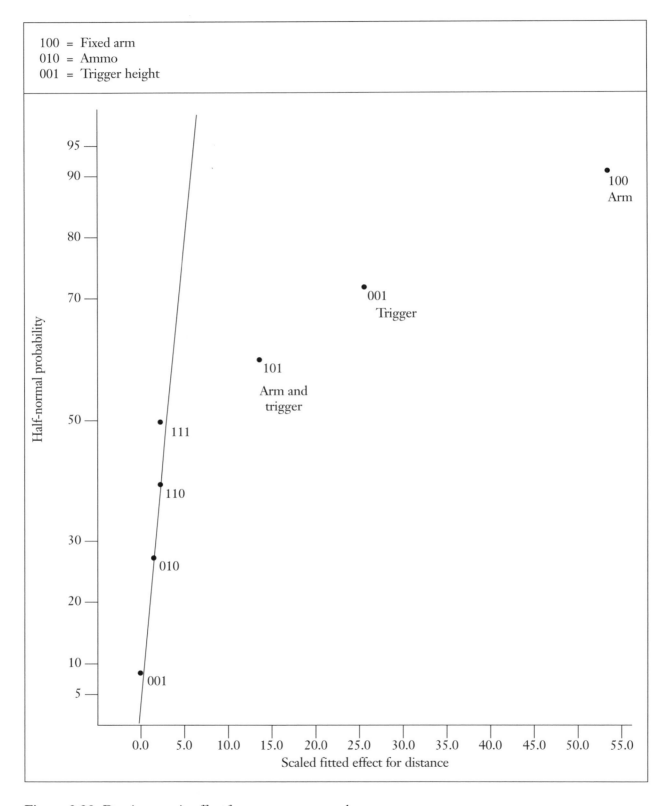

Figure 2.30. Dominant main effect factors pop out on a plot.

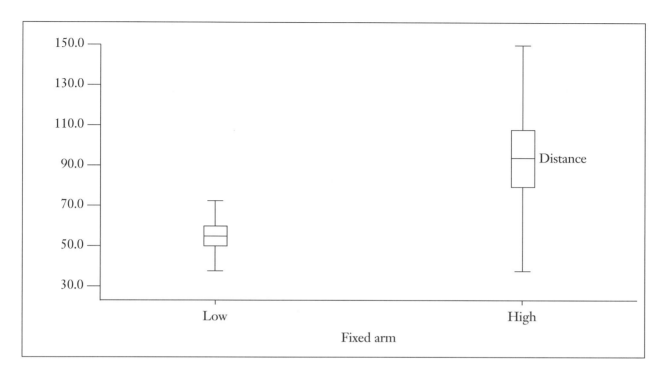

Figure 2.31. Fixed arm height is the important factor.

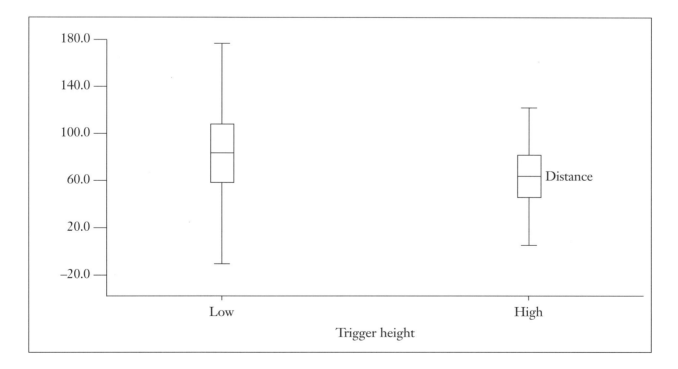

Figure 2.32. Trigger height is a less influential factor.

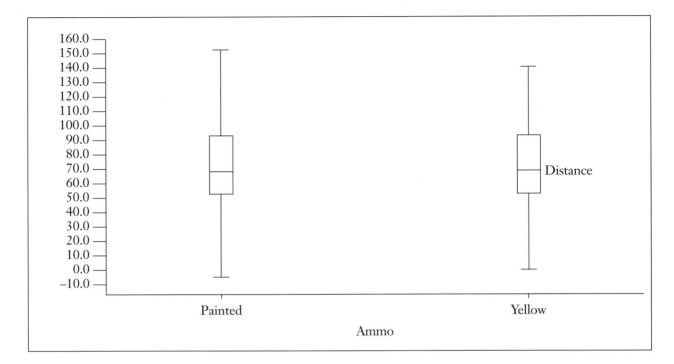

Figure 2.33. Ammo type is not an important factor.

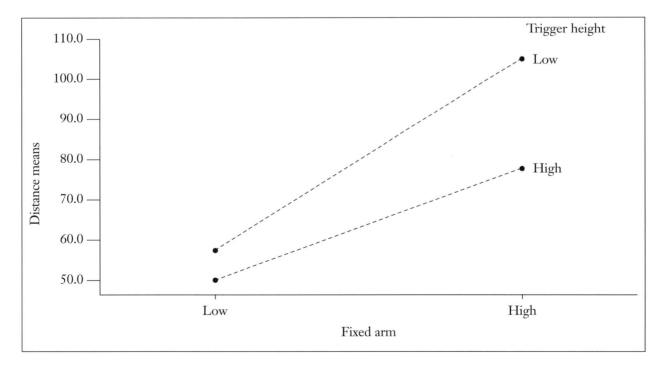

Figure 2.34. Two-factor interaction is important to distance. Visualize each dotted line as a hypothenuse on two separate right triangles. Note that one angle of error is much smaller than the other. The variance between these two angles is significant.

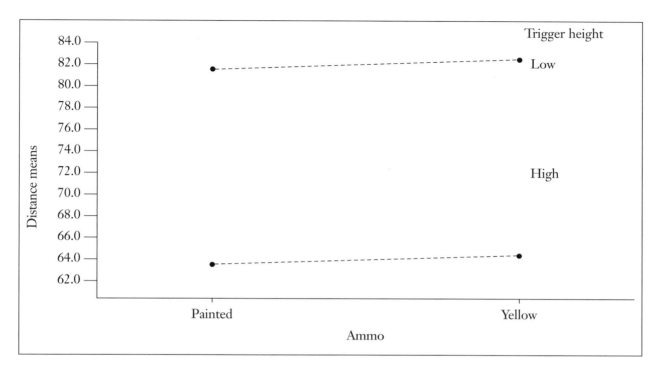

Figure 2.35. There is no interaction between ammo and trigger height. The variance between these two right triangles is not significant. In fact, the parallel and horizontal lines suggest there is almost no variance at all.

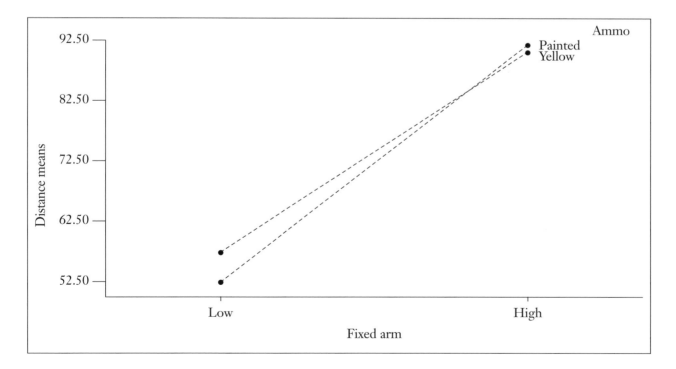

Figure 2.36. There is probably an insignificant arm and ammo interaction.

The final fast-track experiment puts the mathematical, geometrical design-of-experiments model to the test. Can a simple experiment show that the surface area of a parachute has an important effect on flight time? Can it show that a sky diver's weight is important? Would there be a two-factor interaction between the weight of the sky diver and the surface area of the parachute?

The answers to these questions depend on how well you design your experiment. Since many of us are reluctant to jump out of an airplane just to prove that Fisher and Box are right, let's simulate the experiment by using a homemade model. A well-designed experiment will create a wider inductive basis. We will be able to transfer our learning and apply our knowledge in an infinite variety of ways.

Take two differently sized and differently colored handkerchiefs from your dresser drawer. You could use two differently sized napkins or paper towels or whatever fabric you would like. The surface areas are variable x. You will code this variable +1 for one color and –1 for the other color.

Next rig two, 18-inch-long parachute harness lines using the corners of each handkerchief. Use identical nylon or cotton cord on both parachutes to keep the variable homogeneous. Sample homogeneity is a key to success.

Go to the toy closet and select two action figures that are identical in weight, but different in color. Miniature robot figures or dollhouse figurines will do. Code the color of the figure, variable y, +1 for color and –1 for the other. You may choose which is which. You may substitute two bolts of equal weight, pieces of fruit, toothbrushes, or any other "sky diver" you would like. Again, homogeneity is very important to the integrity of your design.

Tape a small object to your sky divers during the experiment. You could use a quarter or a nut that fits the bolt you picked out of your toy closet. The presence or absence of this weight is variable z. Code the experimental runs without the weight as z equals –1. Code the runs with the additional weight as +1. See Figure 2.37 for a sample sky diver experiment template, then create your own in Figure 2.38.

Factors ☞ Runs ▼	x Parachute	y Sky diver	z Coin	Response measure
1	−1 = White	−1 = Black	−1 = No	1.79
2	+1 = Blue	−1 = Black	−1 = No	2.13
3	−1 = White	+1 = Red	−1 = No	2.43
4	+1 = Blue	+1 = Red	−1 = No	2.50
5	−1 = White	−1 = Black	+1 = Yes	1.48
6	+1 = Blue	−1 = Black	+1 = Yes	1.48
7	−1 = White	+1 = Red	+1 = Yes	1.22
8	+1 = Blue	+1 = Red	+1 = Yes	1.64
Sum	0	0	0	

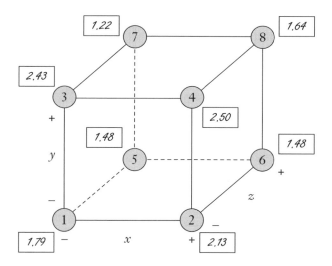

Place each measured response in the appropriate box. Do the values suggest a wider inductive basis for improvement action? Why or why not?

Effects formula: Add four points on a given plane and divide by four. Add four points on the opposite plane and divide by four. Subtract low settings, coded with a minus sign, from high settings, coded with a plus sign. Effect magnitude estimate equals the difference between averages.

$$x = \frac{2+4+6+8}{4} - \frac{1+3+5+7}{4}$$

$$\frac{7.75}{4} \text{ or } 1.93 - \frac{6.92}{4} \text{ or } 1.73$$

$$\boxed{x = .20}$$

$$y = \frac{3+4+7+8}{4} - \frac{1+2+5+6}{4}$$

$$\frac{7.79}{4} \text{ or } 1.9475 - \frac{6.88}{4} \text{ or } 1.72$$

$$\boxed{y = .2275}$$

$$z = \frac{5+6+7+8}{4} - \frac{1+2+3+4}{4}$$

$$\frac{5.82}{4} \text{ or } 1.455 - \frac{8.85}{4} \text{ or } 2.21$$

$$\boxed{z = -.76}$$

Figure 2.37. 2^3 worksheet using sky diver experiment.

Factors ☞ Runs ▼	x Parachute	y Sky diver	z Weight	Response measure
1	−1 =	−1 =	−1 =	
2	+1 =	−1 =	−1 =	
3	−1 =	+1 =	−1 =	
4	+1 =	+1 =	−1 =	
5	−1 =	−1 =	+1 =	
6	+1 =	−1 =	+1 =	
7	−1 =	+1 =	+1 =	
8	+1 =	+1 =	+1 =	
Sum	0	0	0	

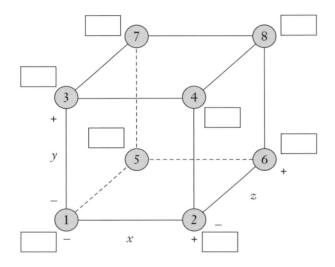

Place each measured response in the appropriate box. Do the values suggest a wider inductive basis for improvement action? Why or why not?

Effects formula: Add four points on a given plane and divide by four. Add four points on the opposite plane and divide by four. Subtract low settings, coded with a minus sign, from high settings, coded with a plus sign. Effect magnitude estimate equals the difference between averages.

$$x = \frac{2 + 4 + 6 + 8}{4} - \frac{1 + 3 + 5 + 7}{4}$$

$$x =$$

$$y = \frac{3 + 4 + 7 + 8}{4} - \frac{1 + 2 + 5 + 6}{4}$$

$$y =$$

$$z = \frac{5 + 6 + 7 + 8}{4} - \frac{1 + 2 + 3 + 4}{4}$$

$$z =$$

Figure 2.38. Blank 2^3 worksheet.

This time we will add a randomization process to the experimental runs. Select eight cards numbered 1, 2, 3, 4, 5, 6, 7, and 8. Shuffle the cards and select them one at a time to determine the order of the runs. If you select run number 7 first, that permutation will be your first experimental run. Deliberate randomization is an important process that can minimize some of the bias that invariably affects every experiment, including designed experiments.

Fall time is the quality you want to measure. These sky divers work pretty well when they are dropped from a height of 30 feet. Use your judgment and imagination. Be sure to use the same drop location for every experimental run. Homogeneity is important.

From experience I can tell you that it helps if only one person serves as the airplane pilot who carries the divers into the air. Enlist another person to serve as the ground crew who times the flights with a stop watch. Fill in the blanks on the template's data array and cube. Notice how the longest flight times in seconds occur with the lightest diver and the largest surface area parachutes. Color, surface area, weight, and flight times are the variables and the measured responses used throughout the theory section of this guide.

Please take some time to ponder the significance of these experiments, the Fisher/Box cube and the important relevance of wide, inductive reasoning. Three variables and any measured response can be tested using this template. Table 2.4 is a small sample of the possible applications that have been used successfully.

As you may have noticed in the last example, the rules of algebra let us substitute a symbol for a number. Qualitative results are not as persuasive as quantitative results, but they work well in a pinch. Go back over the fast-track experiments and replace high values with pluses and low values with minus signs.

You get the idea. Although your inductive inferences are not quite as precise, they are quite similar. *Note:* Short cuts and fast-track experiments are no substitute for expert subject matter knowledge, well-designed experiments, and advanced statistical reasoning skills. You owe it to yourself, as a well-educated adult and a health care leader, to master all three.

Table 2.4. Subject matter categories suitable for designed experiments.

x	y	z	Response
Sleep inducing drug: A or B	Gender: male/female	Age: ≤30 or ≥31	Hours of sleep
Blood transfusion: yes/no	Gender: male/female	Weight: ≤180 or ≥181	Body temperature
Diet supplement: A or B	Gender: male/female	Age: ≤20 or ≥21	Weight gain or loss
Diet supplement: A or B	Gender: male/female	Age: ≤20 or ≥21	Muscle mass
Diet supplement: A or B	Gender: male/female	Age: ≤20 or ≥21	Albumin
Diet supplement: A or B	Gender: male/female	Age: ≤20 or ≥21	Flavor on a 1–10 scale
Latitudes	Longitudes	Altitudes	Annual rainfall in inches
Latitudes	Longitudes	Distance from sun	Average earth temperature/global climate
Hydration: low or high	Soil nutrients: poor or good	Light: low or high	Crop yield
Hydration: low or high	Nutrition: poor or good	Exposure to natural sunlight: low or high	Depression on a 1–10 scale
Aerobic exercise: none or lots	Diet: low fat/high fat	Gender: male/female	Muscle mass
Payor class: Medicare or Medicaid	Length of stay: ≤30 or ≥31	Case manager: registered nurse or physical therapist	Days in accounts receivable
Number of home care therapies: ≤9 or ≥10	Length of stay: ≤30 or ≥31	Case manager: registered nurse or physical therapist	Days in accounts receivable
Stair climber exercise: yes or no	Age: ≤40 or ≥41	Gender: male/female	Respiration rate
Patient education: none/some	Patient access to medical charts: yes/no	Intervention: yes/no	Compliance on a scale 1–10
Gender: male/female	Weight: ≤180 or ≥181	Pressure: c-clamp or manual	Hematoma following cardiac care: Yes = + No = −

Experience teaches nothing without theory. An introduction to theory is presented in the remainder of this book. Do the calculations by hand. Repeat the exercises, and many details of designed experimentation will become clear.

Section II

The Theory of
Designed Experimentation

UNIT THREE

Defining a Single Quality

The most important thing is not testing a hypothesis. It is generating a hypothesis.

—George Box

LEARNING OBJECTIVES

1. Students will understand the importance of the mean as the primary measure of central tendency in a quality statistical analysis.

2. Students will be able to identify an application of the dot plot.

3. Students will understand the importance of the sample standard deviation and standard error as measures of dispersion in a quality statistical analysis.

4. Students will be able to calculate confidence intervals and graph the curve of a t distribution.

A quality characteristic, a measure of process performance, must be operationally defined. The universal statistical measures for defining a quality characteristic are central tendency, dispersion, and probability distribution (see Figure 1.10 on page 24). Applied jointly, these statistics define the parameters of any given quality. Statistical method from the viewpoint of quality control focuses on the relative probabilities of sequential data order. Directed experimentation focuses on the relative probabilities of sequential experimental outcomes in two, three, or more dimensions.

Directed experimentation creates a wider inductive base for deductions. As outlined in Section I, the known benefits of applying this wider inductive basis include economy, the simultaneous study of factor interactions, speed, and a framework for making ethical decisions.

Knowledge of a given quality characteristic prompts additional questions. Improved knowledge produces a higher-quality hypothesis. Expert subject matter knowledge, imagination, and mature judgment power strategic questioning. Expert judgment can be used to determine when it no longer makes good economic sense to investigate a hypothesis.

THE HELICOPTER EXPERIMENT

The Average as a Measure of Central Tendency

The average is the first calculation made in completing a control chart and a design of experiments analysis. The average of a data set is referred to as the process *location*.

Using a helicopter experiment and the lead of Box, Bisgaard, and Fung, we will illustrate the principles of directed experimentation.[1] See Figure 3.1.

Figure 3.1. A quincunx, pretend skydivers, and paper helicopters provide an opportunity to simulate processes and teach categorical thinking.

Construct one paper helicopter using the blueprint provided (see Figure 3.2). Have a friend time four flights as you drop the helicopter from a standing position on a small stepladder or a chair. You may use the flight times in this book to simplify your learning experience. Once you understand experimental reasoning, I encourage you to personally reproduce every experiment in the book so that you can prove the model works exactly as it is described.

The Corrugated Copter Company has a slogan, "Drive down costs." The company has learned that it can decrease the cost of building a helicopter by eliminating the expenses associated with takeoff. Other companies seem to have missed this opportunity entirely. Our master blueprint details this brilliant design in Figure 3.2.

Flight times, y, are measured using a stop watch. The formula for calculating the average flight time $\bar{y}$ is

$$\bar{y} = \frac{\sum_{i=1}^{n} y_i}{n}$$

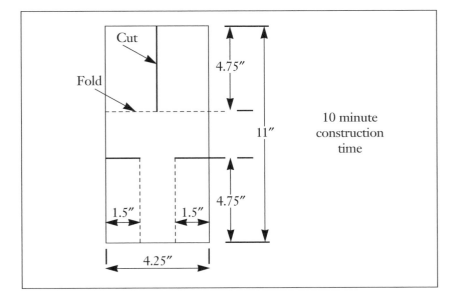

Figure 3.2. Blueprint for a quality helicopter.

The following flight time data were generated using a quincunx. The quincunx produces whole numbers, which, for pedagogical purposes, simplify computation. Simple calculations promote faster learning than complex calculations. (DoE software and computers eliminate the need for manual calculation! They add the dimensions of fun, speed, accuracy, and precision.)

Flight times y

6
10
9
7

$\Sigma = 32$ $\bar{y} = 8$

Induction precedes deduction in the IDEA cycle. The maxim, "count, measure, and draw a picture," holds true in the design of experiments as well as control charting. The difference between control charting and DoE is that DoE data groups, collected sequentially in a process aimed at continuous improvement, are plotted as individual distributions. Since directed experiments are concerned with multiple factors and because they employ blocks, they create, as Fisher suggested in 1935, a wider inductive basis.[2] We can generalize our directed experiment inferences. Experimental results produced under excessively controlled experimental conditions are only relevant under those controlled conditions. (*Controlled* experiment inferences cannot be generalized, regardless of the accepted tradition of doing just that.)

Dot plots are easy. They expose process information quickly. See Figure 3.3 for a sample dot plot. It is interesting to note that in the actual teaching of this plot, Box, Bisgaard, and Fung plot the data prior to calculating the mean! In Box, Hunter, and Hunter's textbook, *Statistics for Experimenters*, the first data plot is a scatter diagram. The second graphic plot plots the data points in sequential order, as in a control chart. The third data plot is the dot diagram.

The average, the arithmetic mean, is the first calculation completed in a quality sciences analysis. This rule is as relevant to the design of experiments as it is to the construction of a

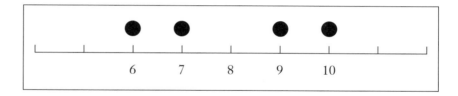

Figure 3.3. A dot plot showing flight time in seconds.

control chart. The second calculation to be completed is the measure of dispersion, the standard deviation. The standard deviation is the root mean square deviation from the mean.[3] The DoE model uses the standard deviation for a sample, which is symbolized with an *s* rather than σ. Table 3.1 shows a variance analysis table for five flight times.

Table 3.1. A variance analysis table for five flight times.

Flight times $= y$	$(y - \bar{y})$	$(y - \bar{y})^2$
6	$6 - 8 = -2$	4
10	$10 - 8 = +2$	4
9	$9 - 8 = 1$	1
7	$7 - 8 = -1$	1
$\Sigma = 32$		$\Sigma (y - \bar{y})^2 = 10$
$n = 4$ $32 \div 4 =$ Average $\bar{y}$ $\bar{y} = 8$		$s^2 = \dfrac{10}{3} = 3.3$ $s^2 = \sqrt{3.3}$ $s = 1.81$
Pythagoras's theorem		
$c^2 = 36 + 100 + 81 + 49$ $= 266$	$a^2 = \bar{y}^2$ $= 64 + 64$ $+ 64 + 64$ $= 256$	$b^2 = 4 + 4 + 1 + 1$ $= 10$
$c^2 = b^2 + a^2$ $266 = 256 + 10$		

This equation is Shewhart's definition of the standard deviation, sigma σ. Usually σ refers to the standard deviation of the population. Philosophically, Shewhart considered the sample to be a population.

$$\sigma = \sqrt{\frac{\sum_{i=1}^{n} (X_i - \bar{X})^2}{n}}$$

This is the Box, Hunter, and Hunter notation for the sample standard deviation.

$$s = \sqrt{\frac{\sum_{i=1}^{n} (y_i - \bar{y})^2}{n - 1}}$$

An additional, important measure of dispersion is now added to the results-based, solution-focused, quality improvement tool kit: the estimated standard deviation of the average $\bar{y}$. The estimated standard deviation of $\bar{y}$ is called the standard error of $\bar{y}$.

$$SE(\bar{y}) = \frac{s}{\sqrt{n}}$$

Thus, for our quincunx-generated data of flight times,

$$SE(\bar{y}) = \frac{s}{\sqrt{n}} = \frac{1.8}{\sqrt{4}} = \frac{1.8}{2} = 0.9$$

The Standard Error

The formula for the standard error provides a cause to pause and ponder the precision of a calculated average. Why is the average so valuable? Why is the standard error so important?

The standard error measures variation in the estimated mean, rather than variation in the individual observations.

Statistical theory and practice demonstrate that averages are less variable than individual data values. In fact, the average of n observations is a more precise characterization of a distribution's mean by a factor of

$$\frac{1}{\sqrt{n}}$$

An idealized dice-rolling example illustrates this phenomenon. Although all models are incomplete, dice rolling is useful in demonstrating many statistical principles. See Figure 3.4 for an example of this principle.

When four consecutive rolls are grouped together, they become a rational subgroup of four. Shewhart recommended subgroup sizes of four when there is no a priori knowledge to justify any other sample size.[4] By averaging the four rolls in this rational subgroup together and plotting them, the standard error of the average is estimated to be half the standard deviation of the individual observations. Averaging predictably improves the characterization of a process average. See Figure 3.5.

$$\frac{1}{\sqrt{n}} = \frac{1}{\sqrt{4}} = \frac{1}{2}$$

Economy and efficiency are common quality improvement values for control charting and design of experiments. The initial precision benefit gain achieved by averaging a group of numbers, n, diminishes as n gets larger. See the following data.

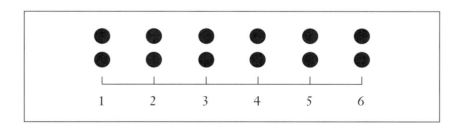

Figure 3.4. The range for 12 individual dice rolls is 5. The "true" theoretical mean of a single die is 3.5.

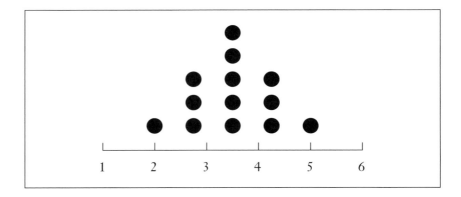

Figure 3.5. As predicted by theory and practice, the dispersion of the average (5 – 2) is 3, almost one-half. The same phenomenon can be illustrated with the quincunx board.

n	$\dfrac{1}{\sqrt{n}}$	
1	1.00	
2	0.71	
3	0.58	
4	0.50	($1/2$) ($\bar{X}$–R control chart subgroup size)
5	0.45	
6	0.41	
7	0.38	
8	0.35	
9	0.33	
16	0.25	
24	0.20	(Rule-of-thumb X, p, np, c, and u control chart threshold sample size)

Following the "count, measure, and draw a picture" instructions, freehand plot the preceding numbers as a curve to illustrate the diminishing return. Scale the y axis, bottom to top, from 0–1.00 in equal increments of .10. Scale the x axis, left to right, from 1–24. See Figure 3.6.

Confidence Limits and the *t* Distribution

With the help of Student's t distribution (detailed in a t table in Table 3.2), the population mean $\bar{y}$, the subgroup size n, the

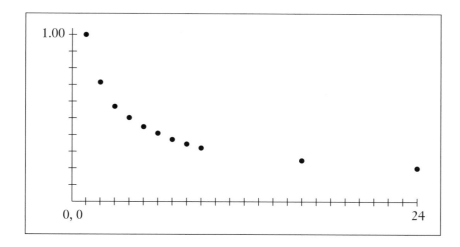

Figure 3.6. The curve begins high, near the *y* axis at the left, and descends as it moves to the right on the *x* axis.

sample standard deviation *s*, and the standard error $\text{SE}(\bar{y})$, we can estimate and graph confidence limits. When graphed, confidence limits help us make a well-calculated, visual, inductive/ deductive inference about the location of the population average.

The *t* distribution is a theoretical distribution, deduced by W. S. Gossett while he worked at the Guiness brewery in Dublin, Ireland.[5] Gossett, who worked as a chemist and published his work under the pseudonym Student, noticed that beer was variable. Beer samples are, usually and relatively speaking, small. Therefore the actual standard deviation of the entire population, σ, cannot be exactly known. Using his imagination, Gossett developed the *t* distribution, the value $t = (y - \bar{y}) \div s$, so that dispersion estimates could be made with small samples.

A small segment of the *t* table, the entire *t* and *z* score tables, is given here (see Table 3.3) so that we can use graphical interpolation to draw a *t* distribution curve. When one uses the sample statistics in the *t* table, the degrees of freedom, symbolized by the letter *v*, help determine the number of observations that are free to vary. The degrees of freedom tell us how many bits of independent data we have to work with.

$$v = n - 1 = \text{degrees of freedom}$$

Table 3.2. z table and t table.

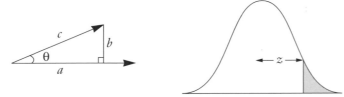

A. Tail area of standard normal distribution. The formula[6] reads "the z score equals one-half the log times the product of [(the number of degrees of freedom about the model error n_E divided by the number of degrees of freedom about the model regression n_R) times the squared cotangent of the angle between the observation vector and the average vector, $\cot^2 \theta$, equals one-half the log of the F ratio," $z = \frac{1}{2} \log [(n_E/n_R) \cot^2 \theta] = \frac{1}{2} \log F$.

z	0.00	0.01	0.02	0.03	0.04	0.05	0.06	0.07	0.08	0.09
0.0	0.5000	0.4960	0.4920	0.4880	0.4840	0.4801	0.4761	0.4721	0.4681	0.4641
0.1	0.4602	0.4562	0.4522	0.4483	0.4443	0.4404	0.4364	0.4325	0.4286	0.4247
0.2	0.4207	0.4168	0.4129	0.4090	0.4052	0.4013	0.3974	0.3936	0.3897	0.3859
0.3	0.3821	0.3783	0.3745	0.3707	0.3669	0.3632	0.3594	0.3557	0.3520	0.3483
0.4	0.3446	0.3409	0.3372	0.3336	0.3300	0.3264	0.3228	0.3192	0.3156	0.3121
0.5	0.3085	0.3050	0.3015	0.2981	0.2946	0.2912	0.2877	0.2843	0.2810	0.2776
0.6	0.2743	0.2709	0.2676	0.2643	0.2611	0.2578	0.2546	0.2514	0.2483	0.2451
0.7	0.2420	0.2389	0.2358	0.2327	0.2296	0.2266	0.2236	0.2206	0.2177	0.2148
0.8	0.2119	0.2090	0.2061	0.2033	0.2005	0.1977	0.1949	0.1922	0.1894	0.1867
0.9	0.1841	0.1814	0.1788	0.1762	0.1736	0.1711	0.1685	0.1660	0.1635	0.1611
1.0	0.1587	0.1562	0.1539	0.1515	0.1492	0.1469	0.1446	0.1423	0.1401	0.1379
1.1	0.1357	0.1335	0.1314	0.1292	0.1271	0.1251	0.1230	0.1210	0.1190	0.1170
1.2	0.1151	0.1131	0.1112	0.1093	0.1075	0.1056	0.1038	0.1020	0.1003	0.0985
1.3	0.0968	0.0951	0.0934	0.0918	0.0901	0.0885	0.0869	0.0853	0.0838	0.0823
1.4	0.0808	0.0793	0.0778	0.0764	0.0749	0.0735	0.0721	0.0708	0.0694	0.0681
1.5	0.0668	0.0655	0.0643	0.0630	0.0618	0.0606	0.0594	0.0582	0.0571	0.0559
1.6	0.0548	0.0537	0.0526	0.0516	0.0505	0.0495	0.0485	0.0475	0.0465	0.0455
1.7	0.0446	0.0436	0.0427	0.0418	0.0409	0.0401	0.0392	0.0384	0.0375	0.0367
1.8	0.0359	0.0351	0.0344	0.0336	0.0329	0.0322	0.0314	0.0307	0.0301	0.0294
1.9	0.0287	0.0281	0.0274	0.0268	0.0262	0.0256	0.0250	0.0244	0.0239	0.0233
2.0	0.0228	0.0222	0.0217	0.0212	0.0207	0.0202	0.0197	0.0192	0.0188	0.0183
2.1	0.0179	0.0174	0.0170	0.0166	0.0162	0.0158	0.0154	0.0150	0.0146	0.0143
2.2	0.0139	0.0136	0.0132	0.0129	0.0125	0.0122	0.0119	0.0116	0.0113	0.0110
2.3	0.0107	0.0104	0.0102	0.0099	0.0096	0.0094	0.0091	0.0089	0.0087	0.0084
2.4	0.0082	0.0080	0.0078	0.0075	0.0073	0.0071	0.0069	0.0068	0.0066	0.0064
2.5	0.0062	0.0060	0.0059	0.0057	0.0055	0.0054	0.0052	0.0051	0.0049	0.0048
2.6	0.0047	0.0045	0.0044	0.0043	0.0041	0.0040	0.0039	0.0038	0.0037	0.0036
2.7	0.0035	0.0034	0.0033	0.0032	0.0031	0.0030	0.0029	0.0028	0.0027	0.0026
2.8	0.0026	0.0025	0.0024	0.0023	0.0023	0.0022	0.0021	0.0021	0.0020	0.0019
2.9	0.0019	0.0018	0.0018	0.0017	0.0016	0.0016	0.0015	0.0015	0.0014	0.0014
3.0	0.0013	0.0013	0.0013	0.0012	0.0012	0.0011	0.0011	0.0011	0.0010	0.0010
3.1	0.0010	0.0009	0.0009	0.0009	0.0008	0.0008	0.0008	0.0008	0.0007	0.0007
3.2	0.0007	0.0007	0.0006	0.0006	0.0006	0.0006	0.0006	0.0005	0.0005	0.0005
3.3	0.0005	0.0005	0.0005	0.0004	0.0004	0.0004	0.0004	0.0004	0.0004	0.0003
3.4	0.0003	0.0003	0.0003	0.0003	0.0003	0.0003	0.0003	0.0003	0.0003	0.0002
3.5	0.0002	0.0002	0.0002	0.0002	0.0002	0.0002	0.0002	0.0002	0.0002	0.0002
3.6	0.0002	0.0002	0.0001	0.0001	0.0001	0.0001	0.0001	0.0001	0.0001	0.0001
3.7	0.0001	0.0001	0.0001	0.0001	0.0001	0.0001	0.0001	0.0001	0.0001	0.0001
3.8	0.0001	0.0001	0.0001	0.0001	0.0001	0.0001	0.0001	0.0001	0.0001	0.0001
3.9	0.0000	0.0000	0.0000	0.0000	0.0000	0.0000	0.0000	0.0000	0.0000	0.0000

Table 3.2. (*continued*).

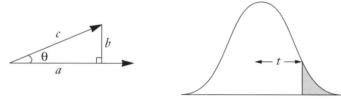

B. Probability points of the t distribution with v degrees of freedom. Fisher's geometry of the t score[7] is $t = \sqrt{F} = \sqrt{n_E/n_R} \cot \theta$.

v	Tail area probability									
	0.4	0.25	0.1	0.05	0.025	0.01	0.005	0.0025	0.001	0.0005
1	0.325	1.000	3.078	6.314	12.706	31.821	63.657	127.32	318.31	636.62
2	0.289	0.816	1.886	2.920	4.303	6.965	9.925	14.089	22.326	31.598
3	0.277	0.765	1.638	2.353	3.182	4.541	5.841	7.453	10.213	12.924
4	0.271	0.741	1.533	2.132	2.776	3.747	4.604	5.598	7.173	8.610
5	0.267	0.727	1.476	2.015	2.571	3.365	4.032	4.773	5.893	6.869
6	0.265	0.718	1.440	1.943	2.447	3.143	3.707	4.317	5.208	5.959
7	0.263	0.711	1.415	1.895	2.365	2.998	3.499	4.029	4.785	5.408
8	0.262	0.706	1.397	1.860	2.306	2.896	3.355	3.833	4.501	5.041
9	0.261	0.703	1.383	1.833	2.262	2.821	3.250	3.690	4.297	4.781
10	0.260	0.700	1.372	1.182	2.228	2.764	3.169	3.581	4.144	4.587
11	0.260	0.697	1.363	1.796	2.201	2.718	3.106	3.497	4.025	4.437
12	0.259	0.695	1.356	1.782	2.179	2.681	3.055	3.428	3.930	4.318
13	0.259	0.694	1.350	1.771	2.160	2.650	3.012	3.372	3.852	4.221
14	0.258	0.692	1.345	1.761	2.145	2.624	2.977	3.326	3.787	4.140
15	0.258	0.691	1.341	1.753	2.131	2.602	2.947	3.286	3.733	4.073
16	0.258	0.690	1.337	1.746	2.120	2.583	2.921	3.252	3.686	4.015
17	0.257	0.689	1.333	1.740	2.110	2.567	2.898	3.222	3.646	3.965
18	0.257	0.688	1.330	1.734	2.101	2.552	2.878	3.197	3.610	3.922
19	0.257	0.688	1.328	1.729	2.093	2.539	2.861	3.174	3.579	3.883
20	0.257	0.687	1.325	1.725	2.086	2.528	2.845	3.153	3.552	3.850
21	0.257	0.686	1.323	1.721	2.080	2.518	2.831	3.135	3.527	3.819
22	0.256	0.686	1.321	1.717	2.074	2.508	2.819	3.119	3.505	3.792
23	0.256	0.685	1.319	1.714	2.069	2.500	2.807	3.104	3.485	3.767
24	0.256	0.685	1.318	1.711	2.064	2.492	2.797	3.091	3.467	3.745
25	0.256	0.684	1.316	1.708	2.060	2.485	2.787	3.078	3.450	3.725
26	0.256	0.684	1.315	1.706	2.056	2.479	2.779	3.067	3.435	3.707
27	0.256	0.684	1.314	1.703	2.052	2.473	2.771	3.057	3.421	3.690
28	0.256	0.683	1.313	1.701	2.048	2.467	2.763	3.047	3.408	3.674
29	0.256	0.683	1.311	1.699	2.045	2.462	2.756	3.038	3.396	3.659
30	0.256	0.683	1.310	1.697	2.042	2.457	2.750	3.030	3.385	3.646
40	0.255	0.681	1.303	1.684	2.021	2.423	2.704	2.971	3.307	3.551
60	0.254	0.679	1.296	1.671	2.000	2.390	2.660	2.915	3.232	3.460
120	0.254	0.677	1.289	1.658	1.980	2.358	2.617	2.860	3.160	3.373
∞	0.253	0.674	1.282	1.645	1.960	2.326	2.576	2.807	3.090	3.291

Quality Health Systems of America, Inc., gratefully acknowledges that these tables are reproduced with the permission of the Biometrika Trustees, Imperial College of Science, Technology, & Medicine, from *Biometrika Tables for Statisticians*, Vol. 3 Third Edition (1966) and Vol. 2 (1972).

Table B is taken from Table III of Fisher and Yates: *Statistical Tables for Biological, Agricultural, and Medical Research 6/e*, published by Addison Wesley Longman Ltd. (1963). Reprinted with permission.

Table 3.3. Probability points of the *t* distribution with *v* degrees of freedom: right-sided tail area probability.

v degrees of freedom	0.4	0.25	0.1	0.05	95-percent confidence 0.025
1	0.325	1.000	3.078	6.314	12.706
2	0.289	0.816	1.886	2.920	4.303
3	0.277	0.765	1.638	2.353	3.182

At v = infinity, the *t* distribution becomes the normal distribution. The *t* distribution, like the normal distribution, is a family of curves. For the family of *t* distribution curves, variability shrinks and density heights lengthen as the sample size increases. See Table 3.2.

Two degrees-of-freedom calculation examples follow.

Example 1. The sum of our flight times samples (6, 10, 9, and 7) is 32. Various combinations of any three numbers in this set can be summed. When three numbers from this set are summed, the fourth number necessarily must be the missing number. If the three numbers are 6, 10, and 9, then

$$
\begin{array}{r}
6 \\
10 \\
+9 \\
\hline
25
\end{array}
$$

$$
\begin{array}{r}
32 \\
-25 \\
\hline
7
\end{array}
$$

In statistical parlance, "one degree of freedom has been lost."

Example 2. Assume that the mean $\bar{y}$ of the four numbers (6, 10, 9, 7) is known to be 8. The absolute deviations from the mean must always total zero. –2, +2, +1, and –1 sum to 0. If the deviations of –2, +2, and +1 are known, then –1 is predetermined. Therefore, one degree of freedom is lost in a sampling problem that uses the standard deviation of the sample because the mean is known.[8]

Confidence limits for the true mean μ are calculated using the following formula.

$$\bar{y} \pm t[\mathrm{SE}(\bar{y})]$$

This can also be written as

$$\bar{y} \pm t\frac{s}{\sqrt{n}}$$

Unless the penalty is hanging, 95-percent confidence (rather than the control chart's 99.73-percent confidence limit) is sufficient grounds for judging whether the values are common to one distribution or whether another, special, distribution is present.

Our quincunx-generated flight time data (6, 10, 9, 7) has yielded an incredible amount of information. The economy of this model is compelling.

$$\bar{y} = 8 \qquad\qquad n = 4 \qquad\qquad \mathrm{SE}(\bar{y}) = 0.9$$
$$s = 1.8 \qquad\qquad v = 3$$

Our confidence limits for μ are

$$8 \pm 3.182 \times 0.9 = 8 \pm 2.8638$$

With 95-percent confidence we can deductively infer that the interval 5.1–10.9 contains μ, the theoretical average. Since we know that whole numbers are the only possibility with a quincunx, we could round off the estimated dispersion measurement range to 5–11. All the observation measurements come from a single quincunx setting. The inductive, statistical inference you have just reached is true.

Count, Measure, and Draw a Picture. For practice, freehand draw both sides of the theoretical t distribution curve for $v = 3$. Figure 3.7 shows a t distribution with 0 as μ. This t distribution curve looks like a slightly flattened-out normal curve.

Now freehand draw the theoretical curve for our flight time data. Dot plot the four flight time values on the abscissa. See Figure 3.8.

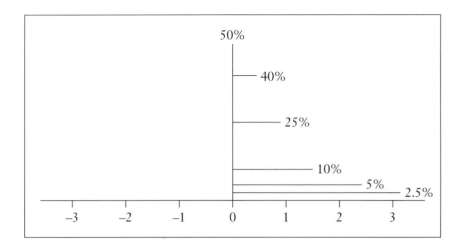

Figure 3.7. Drawing the *t* distribution curve reassures students that statistical methods are empirical. They translate into concrete concepts. Anyone can replicate statistical results.

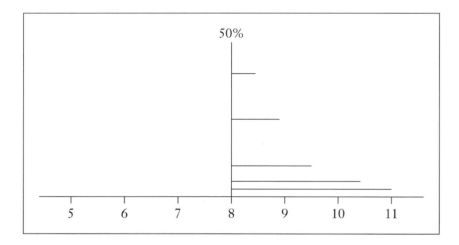

Figure 3.8. Mark the *t* values next to the appropriate horizontal line representing its tail area probability.

Anchor Exercise. Here's an exercise for you. Define the single performance quality for the following flight times: 16, 12, 15, 11. First, dot plot the data. Then, calculate the key data.

$$\bar{y} = \qquad\qquad n = \qquad\qquad \text{SE}(\bar{y}) =$$
$$s = \qquad\qquad v =$$

Next, calculate the 95-percent confidence interval.

$$\bar{y} \pm t\, \frac{s}{\sqrt{n}} = \bar{y} \pm t[\mathrm{SE}(\bar{y})]$$

Finally, graph the curve with a freehand drawing.

UNIT FOUR

Comparing Two Qualities

Now that's a horse of a different color.

—The Mayor of Oz

LEARNING OBJECTIVES

1. Students will learn to use a helicopter analogy, length of flight time data, as a reference for a patient's length of stay.

2. Students will be able to compare two qualities using a t distribution.

3. By repeating some exercises from unit 3, students will become more familiar with the concepts of sampling, blocking, and randomization.

4. Students will learn how to use a quincunx to simulate a process. They will learn the sequential calculation steps in completing a one-way ANOVA.

COMPARISON CATEGORIES

Opinions differ. Casual comparisons frequently create disagreements between people. Strategic questioning and the well-reasoned language of quality science statistical method increase the probability that comparisons will lead to a convergence. This convergence builds agreements instead of arguments. Convergence-building comparisons create political power and commitment. The power of commitment can effect rapid improvement. Convergence and commitment are far more effective than consensus could ever hope to be.

Comparison categories help students transfer learning. See Table 4.1. The skills and knowledge a guitarist has transfer to

Table 4.1. Categorical, allegorical thinking details for the helicopter experiment.

Length of flight versus length of stay	
The surface area of helicopter wings differs.	The surface area of patients differs.
Helicopter colors differ.	People are different colors.
Helicopter weights differ.	People's weights differ.

any number of instruments in the stringed instruments category. Categorical thinking, measurement, analysis skills, and knowledge can also be readily transferred to any number of professional-level questions.

Analogy, similarity in some respects between things that are otherwise dissimilar, is a form of comparison. Metaphor, a figure of speech in which a word or phrase that ordinarily designates one thing is used to designate another, implicitly invites comparison. Analogies and metaphors make learning fun because they engage the imagination. Imaginative, categorical thinking is the essence of rapid improvement.

A comparison of four flight times for a pink and a green helicopter is an analogy. See Table 4.2. What we learn about comparing flight times can be transferred to the comparisons we make in hospitalization, or patient length of stay, times. Time is a universal and categorical measure regardless of context.

The question is which factors, if any, make a difference in the quality we would like to improve? A series of experiments, with the results measured and analyzed, can provide insight, understanding, and additional questions for discovery.

Table 4.2. Experimental data for flight times at Corrugated Copter Company, 7/9/95.

Pink helicopter	Green helicopter
2.32	1.66
2.29	1.78
2.08	1.79
2.25	1.90

HELICOPTER EXPERIMENT:
ARE THE HELICOPTERS DIFFERENT?

After looking at the data, Manager Tom concludes with his usual can-do, let's-get-crackin' attitude, "The measurements are virtually identical." Manager Dick, a conservative who is always ready to please, observes, "The times are very similar." Manager Mary, with an eagle eye on the bottom line, shares her blunt opinion, "Since the times are calculated in seconds and hundredths of seconds, the differences I see are insignificant. We aren't in the business of esoteric research and development. This is a waste of money. Let's get back to production."

As Corrugated Copter's quality leader, you suggest graphing the data before the group goes back into production. See Tables 4.3 and 4.4 and Figure 4.1.

Since everyone has a calculator and knows how to use it, the team decides to calculate the mean and sample standard deviation for each group of data. If they were in upper management, these calculations would have been completed instantaneously as the data were entered into the manager's object-oriented database and personal computing system. See Table 4.3.

$$s = \sqrt{\frac{\sum\limits_{i=1}^{n}(y_i - \bar{y})^2}{n-1}}$$

Table 4.3. Flight time data arrays for the pink and green helicopters.

Pink	Green
2.32	1.66
2.29	1.78
2.08	1.79
2.25	1.90
Total = 8.94	Total = 7.13
$\bar{y}_p$ = 2.235	$\bar{y}_g$ = 1.7825

Table 4.4. Sample standardization for flight times. Note that miniscule differences in calculation answers are due to rounding.

	Pink	
Flight times	$(y - \bar{y})$	$(y - \bar{y})^2$
2.32	2.32 − 2.235 = .085	.0072
2.29	2.29 − 2.235 = .055	.0030
2.08	2.08 − 2.235 = −.155	.0240
2.25	2.25 − 2.235 = .015	.0002
Σ = 8.94		$\Sigma(y - \bar{y})^2$ = .0344
		s_p^2 = .0115
n = 4		s_p = .1071
$\bar{y}$ = 8.94 ÷ 4 = 2.235		
	Green	
Flight times	$(y - \bar{y})$	$(y - \bar{y})^2$
1.66	1.66 − 1.78 = −.12	.0144
1.78	1.78 − 1.78 = .00	.0000
1.79	1.79 − 1.78 = .01	.0001
1.90	1.90 − 1.78 = .12	.0144
Σ = 7.13		$\Sigma(y - \bar{y})^2$ = .0289
		s_g^2 = .0096
n = 4		s_g = .0981
$\bar{y}$ = 7.13 ÷ 4 = 1.7825		

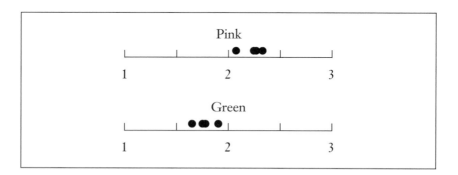

Figure 4.1. The dot plot grabs everyone's attention! There could be a profit opportunity here. Maybe there is a difference between the helicopters.

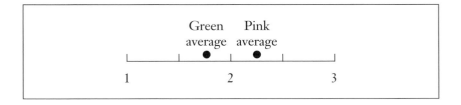

Figure 4.2. A dot plot raises the important questions: Are they differently performing helicopters?

After reviewing their calculations, Manager Tom explains, "They appear to be quite similar." Manager Dick chimes in, "I agree, but they could be a little different." Manager Mary says, "What a waste of time. Let's get back to work and make some money."

As the Corrugated Copter's quality leader you suggest the team establish a reference distribution for an individual mean by pooling variances s_p^2 and s_g^2. Please note that any miniscule differences in the calculation answers you may find are due to rounding.

$$s^2 = \frac{s_p^2 + s_g^2}{2} = \frac{.0115 + .0096}{2} = .0106$$

$$s = \sqrt{s^2} = \sqrt{.0106} = .1027$$

To calculate sample standard deviation $s_{\bar{y}}$, the reference distribution for an individual mean, use the following formula.

$$s_{\bar{y}} = \frac{s}{\sqrt{n}} = \frac{.1027}{\sqrt{4}} = \frac{.1027}{2} = .0514$$

Adding and subtracting two sample standard deviations (.10 in this example) from each individual mean establishes an approximate 95-percent confidence interval length. See Figure 4.3.

We could also use the t distribution to establish a single reference distribution to help us determine if the two helicopter qualities are different. The theoretical mean μ of the t distribution is set at zero. The t values increase with positive values to the right of the mean and decrease with negative values to the

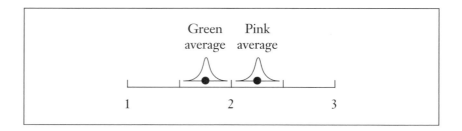

Figure 4.3. When graphed, the reference distributions for the green and pink helicopters, derived for an individual mean, indicate a difference that is due to more than random chance. Think of each distribution curve as a chicken and each mean as an egg. Could one chicken cover both eggs? It is not impossible, but it is highly improbable.

left of the mean. Before we calculate the t value, we must first calculate the standard error. To calculate the standard error of a difference between two sample means, use the following formula.

$$\bar{y}_p - \bar{y}_g = 2.235 - 1.7825 = .4525$$

When each of the two quality experiments have the same number of observations n, use the formula

$$s\sqrt{\frac{2}{n}}$$

Therefore,

$$\mathrm{SE}(\bar{y}_p - \bar{y}_g) = s\sqrt{\frac{2}{n}} = .1027\sqrt{\frac{2}{4}} = (.1027)(.7071) = .0726$$

And the value of T,

$$T = \frac{(\bar{y}_p - \bar{y}_g)}{\mathrm{SE}(\bar{y}_p - \bar{y}_g)} = \frac{.4525}{.0726} = 6.23278$$

Find the approximate location of this value in the t table in unit 3. The exceptionally large T reassures us that these helicopter differences are statistically significant; however, one number does not give us a complete picture of the probable dispersion of data. So, using the t table with the following formula, we can calculate the 95-percent confidence interval for the differences in the means.

$$95\text{-percent confidence} = (\bar{y}_\text{p} - \bar{y}_\text{g}) \pm t_{v=6} \times \text{SE}(\bar{y}_\text{p} - \bar{y}_\text{g})$$

$$= .4525 \pm (2.447 \times .0726)$$

$$= .4525 \pm .1777$$

The decision rule for determining if there is one or two distributions is as follows. If the theoretical mean for the t distribution, zero, lies within the confidence limits, there is no significant difference. Our confidence limit values are .2748 to .6302. The entire interval lies to the right of zero. We can reasonably infer that the difference between the helicopters is due to more than random chance. Draw a small t-distribution curve to illustrate the confidence limits.

THE ANALYSIS OF VARIANCE

ANOVA provides a formal mathematical model for calculating and tracking the sums of squares and degrees of freedom. Personal computing power removes the laborious calculation task that an ANOVA requires. Nevertheless, understanding how this model works and why it works, and knowing that it does work extraordinarily well in the context of a designed experiment, provide some insight that is important to subject mastery.[1] Understanding the limitations of ANOVA is also important to understanding the difference between applied statistical practice and academic theory.

1. ANOVA provides a qualitative, yes/no answer. The rich, quantitative illustrations afforded by graphical depiction are absent from ANOVA. Intuition and imagination sparks fly faster with graphics than without them. Statistical pictures promote contemplation.

2. There is a difference between statistical significance and practical significance.[2] Sometimes large effects are not statistically significant. The first bar graph example presented in unit 1 is an example. Quality improvement requires continuous experimentation and the continual replication of results. Highly reliable processes that are capable of reproducing very consistent results may have significant economic value, even if the results of an ANOVA study are not statistically significant.

3. ANOVA assumptions are frequently invalidated. Assumptions of normality are often incorrect. Any assumption that the variability of the response variable is the same for all points in the experimental design is vulnerable.

4. Academic, theoretical, statistical work can be, and usually is, quite rigid. An experimenter is expected to state a formal hypothesis, test the hypothesis in a traditional way, and report results based on a predetermined test statistic.[3] The needs to create a profit, pay salaries, and develop new products in competitive markets are generally absent. The importance of nurturing a prosperous enterprise and creating new jobs usually is an irrelevant concern.

In real life, on-the-job experimentation has an aim: "Create a constancy of purpose toward improvement, with the aim of becoming competitive and to stay in business and to provide jobs."[4] In real life, experimenters can and often must complete confirmatory runs. Experimenters can, must, and are obligated to continuously explore new opportunities as they occur. Working experimenters improve quality continuously to reduce costs.

Experimenters who work for a living must use their imaginations to find solutions, new markets, and new hypotheses. Since puzzle-solving time is precious, these experimenters use a software application to automate ANOVA calculation.

The following handwork ANOVA process is included to illustrate what the computer is doing. It can help you understand what ANOVA results mean.

As Box, Hunter, and Hunter explain, "The additive property of the sum of the squares arises because of the algebraic identity (true for any set of data whatever: clinical, financial, or operational data)."[5] The vectors and geometry associated with the analysis of variance are due to the orthogonality in the Pythagorean theorem: The sum of the squares of the legs of a right triangle equals the square of the hypotenuse. The hypotenuse of a right triangle is the side opposite the 90° angle. See Figure 4.4.

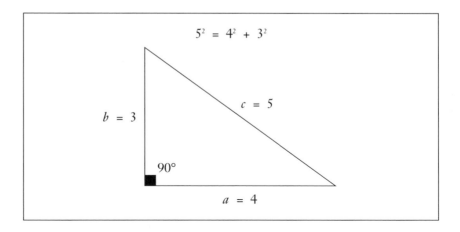

Figure 4.4. Orthogonality and the Pythagorean theorem give structural integrity to directed experiments.

When used on a daily basis, the design of experiments can teach one how to think in multiple dimensions. DoE teaches us how to define quality systematically, in n dimensions, through the constant passage of time.

$$\sum_{t=1}^{k}\sum_{i=1}^{n_t}(y_{ti}-\overline{y})^2 = \sum_{t=1}^{k}n_t(\overline{y}_t-\overline{y})^2 + \sum_{t=1}^{k}\sum_{i=1}^{n_t}(y_{ti}-\overline{y}_t)^2$$

This sum of squares algebraic equation means

$$S_D = S_T + S_R$$

And in everyday English, courtesy of Box, Hunter, and Hunter,

Total sum of squares of deviations from the grand average	=	Between-treatment sum of squares	+	Within-treatment (residual) sum of squares

The simple quadratic equation from geometry is detailed below. In Fisher's language of designed experimentation, the use of small samples yields sufficient statistics. A sufficient statistic—an arithmetic mean and its theoretical distribution—allows us to make useful estimates.[6] Box, Hunter, and Hunter's explanation of the geometric interpretation of the ANOVA shows how an observation vector *y* equals the term *c*. They show how the corresponding grand average represents vector *a*, and the remaining vector *b* equals the deviations from the grand average.[7] They use different letters, but algebra is a purposely flexible language.

$$c^2 = a^2 + b^2$$

Steps to Create an ANOVA

A quincunx allows us to simulate a process to demonstrate this formal model. The form (see Figure 4.5) and the sequential instructions for calculating the difference between two qualities were developed by Robert Carey of American Quality Resources. It is used here with his written permission and the permission of Jim Warren of Lightening Calculator.

1. Generate three sets of data with 10 observations in each set. The funnel is set at three different locations at the top of the quincunx. To save time, the data and all the answers are already recorded in the appropriate boxes. Although you could enter this data into your spreadsheet application and complete the exercise in 10 seconds, this choice will not teach you what you need to know about ANOVA. Use the blank form in Figure 4.5 to practice. Figure 4.6 has the answers.

2. Code the data. Coding will make squaring the values easier. Code the smallest observed value, 0. Our smallest observed value (SOV) is 6. Subtract 6 from all observations and place the answer to each subtraction problem in the brackets [ ].

3. Sum the coded values for each level of factor *A*. Place the total within the bracket labeled level sum.

4. Calculate the level average for each level of factor *A*. Place your answer in the appropriate bracket. *Note:* At this point if you added 6 to this coded value, you would have the decoded level averages.

5. Add the three totals to determine the grand total. Place your answer in the box labeled GT.

6. Count the number of total observations (*N*) for all three tests and record this number in the box labeled *N*. (Yes, the answer is 30!)

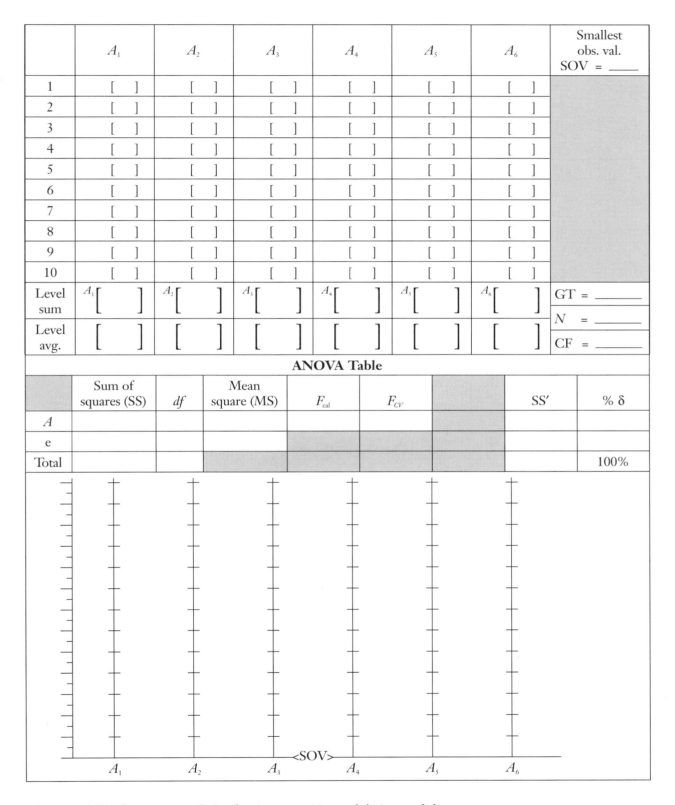

Figure 4.5. Blank one-way analysis of variance experimental design worksheet.

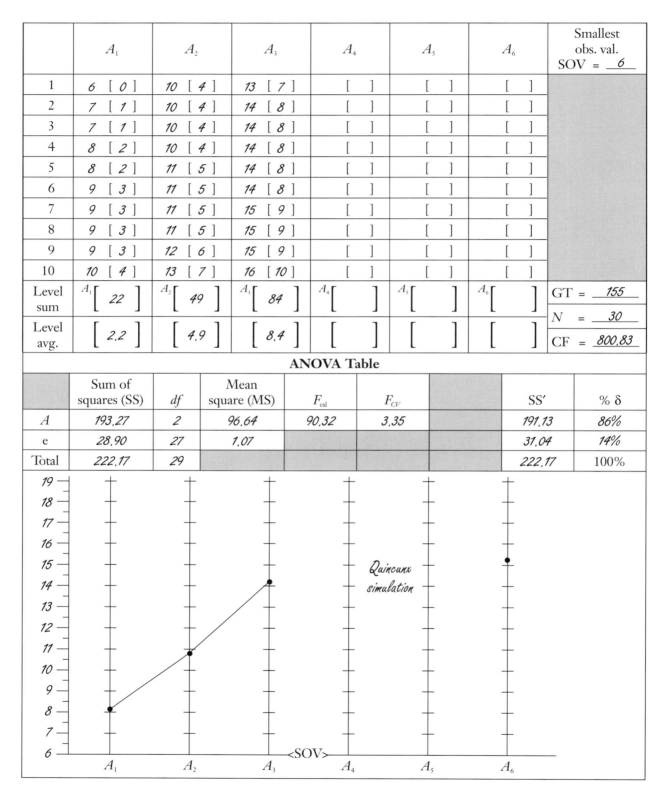

	A_1	A_2	A_3	A_4	A_5	A_6	Smallest obs. val. SOV = 6
1	6 [0]	10 [4]	13 [7]	[ ]	[ ]	[ ]	
2	7 [1]	10 [4]	14 [8]	[ ]	[ ]	[ ]	
3	7 [1]	10 [4]	14 [8]	[ ]	[ ]	[ ]	
4	8 [2]	10 [4]	14 [8]	[ ]	[ ]	[ ]	
5	8 [2]	11 [5]	14 [8]	[ ]	[ ]	[ ]	
6	9 [3]	11 [5]	14 [8]	[ ]	[ ]	[ ]	
7	9 [3]	11 [5]	15 [9]	[ ]	[ ]	[ ]	
8	9 [3]	11 [5]	15 [9]	[ ]	[ ]	[ ]	
9	9 [3]	12 [6]	15 [9]	[ ]	[ ]	[ ]	
10	10 [4]	13 [7]	16 [10]	[ ]	[ ]	[ ]	
Level sum	A_1 [22]	A_2 [49]	A_3 [84]	A_4 [ ]	A_5 [ ]	A_6 [ ]	GT = 155
Level avg.	[2.2]	[4.9]	[8.4]	[ ]	[ ]	[ ]	N = 30 CF = 800.83

ANOVA Table

	Sum of squares (SS)	df	Mean square (MS)	F_{cal}	F_{CV}		SS′	% δ
A	193.27	2	96.64	90.32	3.35		191.13	86%
e	28.90	27	1.07				31.04	14%
Total	222.17	29					222.17	100%

Figure 4.6. One-way analysis of variance experimental design worksheet with answers.

7. Calculate the correction factor (CF). The formula for the CF is

$$CF = GT^2 \div N =$$

8. Calculate the coded sum of squares for treatments using the three-level sums and the following formula.

$$[(A_1^2 + A_2^2 + A_3^2) \div 10] - CF =$$

Place this value in the sum of squares A box.

9. Calculate the coded sum of squares total (SS_{tot}) using each coded value and the following formula. There are 30 observations so this will take a bit of time.

$$SS_{tot} = (X_1^2 + X_2^2 + X_3^2 \ldots X_N) - CF$$
$$= (0^2 + 1^2 + 1^2 \ldots 9^2 + 10^2) - CF$$

Place this value in the sum of squares (SS) total box.

10. Calculate the sum of squares error for the coded data (SS_e) using the following formula.

$$SS_e = SS_{tot} - SS_{A\,box}$$

Place this answer in the box labeled e under the sum of squares (SS) column.

11. Calculate the degrees of freedom df for A, total, and error, e, using the following formulas. (The layout for this column of three numbers can make this step a bit confusing, so be careful with your thinking.)

$$df_A = (\text{number of levels}) - 1$$
$$= 3 - 1 = 2$$
$$df_{tot} = (\text{total number of observations}) - 1$$
$$= 30 - 1 = 29$$
$$df_e = df_{tot} - df_A$$
$$= 29 - 2 = 27$$

12. Calculate the mean square values for factor A (the A box) and error, e.

$$MS_A = SS_A \div df_A$$
$$MS_e = SS_e \div df_e$$

Place the answers in the appropriately labeled box on the form.

13. Calculate the F ratio for factor A.

$$F \text{ ratio } = MS_A \div MS_e$$

Place this answer in the F_{cal} box. The critical F value for 95-percent confidence, taken from an F table, is 3.355. See Box, Hunter, and Hunter's text for the definitive list of F values.] Factor A (the funnel position in the quincunx) is significant if our F ratio is larger than 3.355.

14. Calculate the percent contribution, signified by the Greek letter ρ, of factor A and the error to the total observed variation. To do this we must first calculate some adjusted values for sum of squares A (SS_A) and SS_e. Place the values in the appropriate ANOVA table box.

$$SS_A' = SS_A - df_A (MS_e)$$
$$SS_e' = SS_{tot} - SS_A'$$
$$\%\rho_A = SS_A' \div SS_{tot}$$
$$\%\rho_e = SS_e' \div SS_{tot}$$

15. Scale and plot the graph. The smallest observed value scaling on the abscissa is completed for you. By plotting the coded level averages, those values are translated back into the estimated averages of the funnel location on the quincunx.

We now know that factor A, the funnel position I set to generate the three sets of data, is significant. We have an estimated average for each setting, and the estimates are correct. We have spent a lot of time and we do not have a very rewarding graphic image. Personal computing removes the drudgery and gives us the total picture in an instant.

Comparing Three Qualities

Three of a kind beat a pair.

—A poker axiom

LEARNING OBJECTIVES

1. Students will reinforce their learning by repeating the fundamentals of data analysis.

2. Students will learn to transfer their learning on comparing two qualities to comparing three qualities: flight time for pink, green, and white helicopters.

3. Students will learn how to plot residuals for confounded experimental blocks.

4. Students will be able to graph a distribution using normal probability paper.

HELICOPTER EXAMPLE: SOME PRACTICE COMPARING QUALITIES

Directed experimentation lets us simultaneously compare three or more treatments. The reference interval technique we learned in prior units helps us achieve this higher-order analysis. Two new vocabulary words, *confounding* and *residuals*, will be introduced as concepts at the end of this unit. We will continue to study our fictitious company, Corrugated Copters.

Corrugated Copters is taking the market by storm. The company is testing prototypes to ensure that customers get as long a flight time as possible. Three sets of experimental data are summarized in Table 5.1. From the last set of experiments, Corrugated Copter's R&D team is converging on the obvious fact that pink helicopters seem to stay airborne longer.

99

Table 5.1. Comparison of pink, green, and white helicopters' flight times.

	Pink	Green	White
Run #1	2.33	1.65	1.79
Run #2	2.28	1.75	1.75
Run #3	2.10	1.80	1.70
Run #4	2.24	1.89	1.81

Manager Tom calculates and graphs the measurements in his head to save time and money, "These pink helicopters are hot. Fashion-conscious people love pink, and we could clean up. Everyone knows pink downhill skis are the best performers!" Manager Dick joins in, "I think I like pink a little bit too." Manager Mary suggests an aggressive action plan, "Let's manufacture 100 percent pink helicopters. We could save a lot of time that way, and make a lot of money. Time is money, I always say."

As the company's quality guru, you suggest a few basics. First you plot the data as Figure 5.1 shows. You also remind people to get out those calculators. We might learn something, and since knowledge is worth so much, maybe the process will be profitable. Work through the calculations again to reinforce your learning. First, determine the sample standard deviation. Then see Tables 5.2, 5.3, and 5.4. Remember that minute differences in the answers are due to rounding.

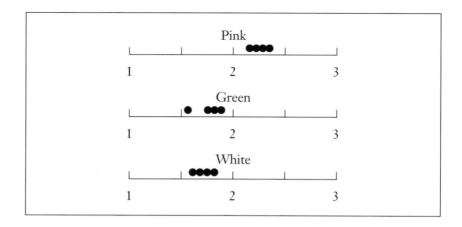

Figure 5.1. Pink helicopters do seem to perform better than green and white helicopters. But with so many data points, perhaps it is all just one big population of helicopters.

Table 5.2. Pink helicopters—sample standard deviation for y_p.

Flight times	$(y - \bar{y})$	$(y - \bar{y})^2$
2.33	2.33 − 2.2375 = .0925	.0086
2.28	2.28 − 2.2375 = .0425	.0018
2.10	2.10 − 2.2375 = −.1375	.0189
2.24	2.24 − 2.2375 = .0025	.00001
Σ = 8.95		$\Sigma(y - \bar{y})^2$ = .0293
n = 4		s_p = .0988
$\bar{y}$ = 8.95 ÷ 4 = 2.2375		

Table 5.3. Green helicopters—sample standard deviation for y_g.

Flight times	$(y - \bar{y})$	$(y - \bar{y})^2$
1.65	1.65 − 1.7725 = −.1225	.0150
1.75	1.75 − 1.7725 = −.0225	.0005
1.80	1.80 − 1.7725 = .0275	.0008
1.89	1.89 − 1.7725 = .1175	.0138
Σ = 7.09		$\Sigma(y - \bar{y})^2$ = .0310
n = 4		s_g = .1001
$\bar{y}$ = 7.09 ÷ 4 = 1.7725		

Table 5.4. White helicopters—sample standard deviation for y_w.

Flight times	$(y - \bar{y})$	$(y - \bar{y})^2$
1.79	1.79 − 1.7625 = .0275	.0008
1.75	1.75 − 1.7625 = −.0125	.0002
1.70	1.70 − 1.7625 = −.0625	.0039
1.81	1.81 − 1.7625 = .0475	.0023
Σ = 7.05		$\Sigma(y - \bar{y})^2$ = .0072
n = 4		s_w = .0486
$\bar{y}$ = 7.05 ÷ 4 = 1.7625		

$$s = \sqrt{\frac{\sum_{i=1}^{n}(y_i - \bar{y})^2}{n - 1}}$$

Plot the three averages and freehand draw their distributions to include two sample standard deviations on each side of the mean. See Figure 5.2.

A calculated reference interval helps us determine whether the discrepancies between the three averages are greater than would reasonably be expected from the variation that occurs within each product.[1] The following sequence of five calculations and a dot plot give us insight.

1. Pool the individual variances. The number of qualities being considered is 3. Note that you must use the sample standard deviation formula to calculate the variances, which were specifically not included in the preceding tables.

$$s_{pooled}^2 = \frac{s_p^2 + s_g^2 + s_w^2}{3}$$

$$= \frac{.0098 + .01 + .0023}{3}$$

$$= \frac{.0221}{3} = .0074$$

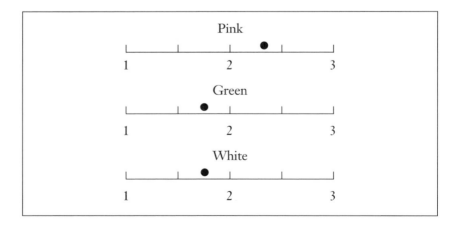

Figure 5.2. What are your deductions regarding the performance of these three helicopters?

The pooled standard deviation, s_{pooled}, is the square root of the pooled variance.

$$s_{pooled} = \sqrt{.0074} = .0858$$

2. Calculate the scale factor for the reference interval. The number of observations per helicopter is 4.

$$\text{scale factor} = s_{\bar{y}} = \frac{s_{pooled}}{\sqrt{4}} = \frac{.0858}{2} = .0429$$

3. Add the degrees of freedom v associated with s_{pooled}: $v = 3 + 3 + 3 = 9$.

4. Find the correct t value on page 79 for $v = 9$ degrees of freedom and 95-percent confidence (0.025 tail probability on each side of the mean.) For this problem $t = 2.262$.

5. Calculate the end points of the reference interval.

$$\eta \pm t \times \text{scale factor} = \eta \pm 2.262 \times .0429 = \eta \pm .0971$$

The interval, .0971, must be multiplied by 2 so that the reference interval ends are equidistant from the theoretical mean, η. The interval width is only .1942!

6. Plot the interval and imaginary distribution curve on a dot plot. See Figure 5.3. Imagine sliding the reference interval back and forth over the averages to judge which are the same and which are different. In other words, if the reference interval was the bottom of a skinny chicken, could she cover all of the eggs?

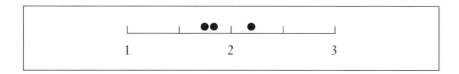

Figure 5.3. Can one distribution reference interval cover all the data points? The answer is no.

PREVENTING DESIGNED EXPERIMENT PROBLEMS AND SOLVING THEM

Bad news! After all our work, the team discovers pink flights were run at Paine Field in Everett, Washington. The green flights were run at Sea-Tac International Airport in Seattle. The white flights were run at Boeing Field. To make matters worse, all of the run 1 data were collected on Monday. Run 2 happened

Tuesday. Run 3 was scheduled Wednesday, and run 4 data were collected on Thursday. Our color settings are confounded (confused) with our airfield locations. The day of the week may be an important factor. Relabel the data accordingly. See Table 5.5.

With this new information, what can we now conclude about the flight times? Obviously we are less certain about our inferences. Wind conditions, temperature, observation errors, and other experimental noise may have affected our results more than helicopter color. Fortunately, all is not necessarily lost.

Randomization, a process we used with the fast-track skydiving experiment, could have helped us prevent our confounding problems. We should have let the computer software program randomize the order of the experimental runs for us. We did not complete this process, so we may have ruined what's been done.

In the health care industry, the unexpected and unpredictable order of patients arriving in the hospital or doctor's office is a fairly reliable randomizer in its own right. With experience you will learn to use your judgment to spot the occasions that call for an extra-special effort to randomize experimental runs for hospital patients or helicopter flights.

In addition to our location and days-of-the-week disasters, we now discover that Manager Mary ran all the experiments. We know she is biased. She could have fixed the outcome of the experiment! We decide to trust her integrity and move forward. Since we know what days of the week the flights took place, we could treat the days of the week as experimental blocks. We could then examine the data from these blocks by using a simple dot plot called a *residual plot*.

Table 5.5. Comparison of helicopter flight times with additional factors.

	Pink: Paine Field	Green: Sea-Tac	White: Boeing Field
Monday	2.33	1.65	1.79
Tuesday	2.28	1.75	1.75
Wednesday	2.10	1.80	1.70
Thursday	2.24	1.89	1.81

Residual plots can help us diagnose data and design problems. Residual plots can also help us expose other analysis problems. A *residual* is the difference between the actual observation and the best prediction of that observation, the group average.

Note that the residual sums in Tables 5.6 and 5.7 equal zero. The Pythagorean theorem lets us interpret the algebraic sum of

Table 5.6. Original data array and residual data array for flight times, blocked by field.

	Pink: Paine Field	Green: Sea-Tac	White: Boeing Field
Monday	2.33	1.65	1.79
Tuesday	2.28	1.75	1.75
Wednesday	2.10	1.80	1.70
Thursday	2.24	1.89	1.81
Sum Σ	8.95	7.09	7.05
Average	2.2375	1.7725	1.7625
Residuals for data grouped by field/color			
Monday	.0925	−.1225	.0275
Tuesday	.0425	−.02250	−.0125
Wednesday	−.1375	.02750	−.0625
Thursday	.0025	.11750	.0475
Residual sum Σ	0	0	0

Table 5.7. Original data array and residual data array for flight times, blocked by days of the week.

Data grouped by days of the week				Sum	Average
Monday	2.33	1.65	1.79	5.77	1.92333
Tuesday	2.28	1.75	1.75	5.78	1.92667
Wednesday	2.10	1.80	1.70	5.6	1.86667
Thursday	2.24	1.89	1.81	5.94	1.98
Residuals grouped by days of the week				Residual sums	
Monday	.40667	−.27333	−.13333	0	
Tuesday	.35333	−.17667	−.17667	0	
Wednesday	.23333	−.06667	−.16667	0	
Thursday	.26000	−.09000	−.17000	0	

the squares, the ANOVA, for these data sets. As Fisher explained in technical detail, and Box, Hunter, and Hunter state in simple English, "the additive property of the sum of the squares arises because of the algebraic identity (true for any set of data whatever.)"[2] Algebraic expressions can be graphed using geometry. This truth is so simple it is profound. They are absolutely, categorically, and allegorically correct.

Figure 5.4 is a schematic of what Fisher imagined.[3] This three-dimensional drawing tacitly implies that the designed experimentation model works in any space of n dimensions. If my own learning curve can serve as a standard, staring at the geometry of a cut diamond makes Fisher's vision easier to imagine. It took about six months of meditation before this image appeared of its own accord, sparkles and all, during an actual analysis. Repetition is important to learning. DoE repetition is so beautiful and rewarding that the imagination/analysis process soon becomes a habit.

Our 12 flight data times let us test the arithmetic in a 12-dimensional model. The final answers in Table 5.8 are equal to a whole number plus one decimal place. The inevitable rounding discrepancies that emerge from squaring and square root calculations to fifth decimal place are included as a reminder.

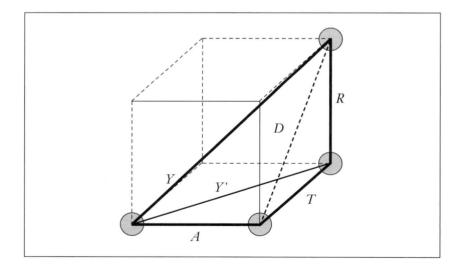

Figure 5.4. Geometry holds an ANOVA together in context. The observation vector Y, the grand average A, and deviations from the grand average D form one right triangle. The 90° angle formed by treatment deviations and residuals shares vector D.

Table 5.8. Arithmetic display of data from three helicopter experiments.

	Observations = y_{ti} treatment = t			Grand average + ($\bar{y}$)			Treatment deviations + ($\bar{y}_t - \bar{y}$)			Residuals (within-treatment deviations) ($y_{ti} - \bar{y}_t$)		
	1	2	3									
	2.33	1.65	1.79	1.92417	1.92417	1.92417	.31333	-.15167	-.16167	.0925	-.1225	.0275
	2.28	1.75	1.75	1.92417	1.92417	1.92417	.31333	-.15167	-.16167	.0425	-.0225	-.0125
	2.10	1.80	1.70	1.92417	1.92417	1.92417	.31333	-.15167	-.16167	-.1375	.0275	-.0625
	2.24	1.89	1.81	1.92417	1.92417	1.92417	.31333	-.15167	-.16167	.0025	.1175	.0475
Average $\bar{y}$	2.2375	1.7725	1.7625									
Grand average	1.92417											
Vector—each one has 12 elements	$Y =$			$A +$			$T +$			R		
Sum of squares = squared length of each vector	45.0847 =			44.42901 +			.58927 +			.066425		
Degrees of freedom = number of dimensions in which the vector is constrained to lie.	12 =			1 +			2 +			9		

Y, the expected observation values of a linear equation if the model is correct and the vector that transverses the cube along its bottom plane, is a function of A and T. Each of the right triangles in Figure 5.4 follows the formula $c^2 = a^2 + b^2$.

Everything varies, including equivalent answers. Fisher's imaginative model and computations are truly astonishing when one recalls he had blind-as-a-bat eyesight and he worked without the benefit of a desktop computing system.

Residuals should be plotted in every rational and reasonable way to expose design problems or significant data differences that may be hidden from an intuitive viewpoint. Vector representation produces insight and an improved understanding of the counts and measures we make of the process we are observing. Grouping data into different blocks produces a new set of residual values and a new set of perspectives. Even a set of simple residual dot plots for our two types of blocks, days of the week and flight locations, can add depth to our helicopter flight time analysis. See Figures 5.5, 5.6, and 5.7.

Calculated reference intervals add the necessary precision to residual analysis. Box, Bisgaard, and Fung outline a 10-step calculation and data-plotting process.[4] Field experience has shown that even the simplified seven-step, step-by-step explanation of an analysis of residuals is a challenging transfer of knowledge process for teacher as well as student. Since one cannot ask a book a question, it is important to locate a qualified teacher who understands the relationship of geometry and the analysis of variance.

Time, frequent repetition, and a careful review of the patterns found in a data array are important to learning. Learning to use t-table values is an essential step in understanding the theory and practical application of designed experiment theory.

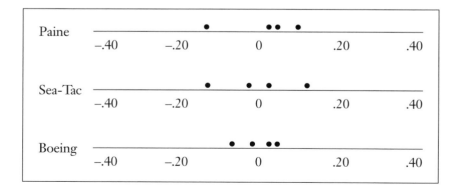

Figure 5.5. Flight time residual plots from Table 5.6 are evenly distributed about the central value, zero, for all flight locations. A different color helicopter was flown at each location.

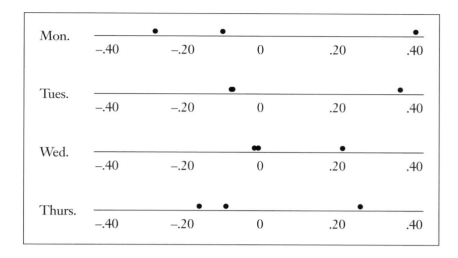

Figure 5.6. The four outlier residuals from Table 5.7 each come from the first flight time, the pink helicopter flight times. Something seems to be different about these flights.

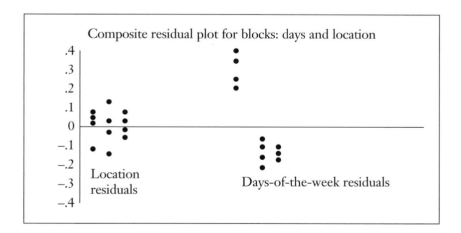

Figure 5.7. The differences between the first and second residual number sets suggests that something is different about the pink helicopters, which we renamed for the Paine field location.

Seven-Step Explanation of Analysis of Residuals

1. Use the data array for the days-of-the-week block to calculate the average for each column. See Table 5.9.

2. Calculate the adjusted residuals r from the new block set, days of the week, by subtracting the column average from each data point in the column. See Table 5.10. The sum for each column now equals zero. The sum for each row

Table 5.9. Residuals days of the week.

				Residual sums
Monday	.4067	−.2733	−.1333	0
Tuesday	.35333	−.17667	−.17667	0
Wednesday	.2333	−.06667	−.16667	0
Thursday	.26	−.09	−.17	0
Total	1.25336	−.60664	−.64664	
Average	.31333	−.15167	−.16167	

Table 5.10. Residuals days of the week and adjusted residuals r for days-of-the-week blocks.

Residuals				Residual sums
Monday	.4067	−.2733	−.1333	0
Tuesday	.35333	−.17667	−.17667	0
Wednesday	.2333	−.06667	−.16667	0
Thursday	.26	−.09	−.17	0
Total	1.25336	−.60664	−.64664	0
Average	.31334	−.15166	−.16166	0
Adjusted residuals				Residual sums
Monday	.09333	−.12167	.02833	0
Tuesday	.04000	−.02500	−.01500	0
Wednesday	−.08000	.08500	−.00500	0
Thursday	−.05333	.06167	−.00833	0
Total	0	0	0	0

also equals zero at three decimal places. Everything varies. Remember that each column represents the flight times of three different helicopters, which we have renamed for the air field the helicopters flew from.

3. Calculate the adjusted residual number sets sample variance s^2 and the data's sample standard deviation s using the following formula. The formula means that the sample variance of the adjusted residuals equals the sum of the

squares of the adjusted residuals divided by the product of the degrees of freedom for the treatments, the columns, times the degrees of freedom for the days of the week blocks, the rows. See Table 5.11. r^2 = adjusted residuals.

$$s^2 = \frac{\Sigma r^2}{(\text{Columns} - 1)(\text{Blocks} - 1)} = \frac{\Sigma r^2}{(3 - 1)(4 - 1)}$$

$$s^2 = \frac{.04715}{6} = .00786$$

$$s = \sqrt{.00786} = .08865$$

4. Use the degrees of freedom, 6, and the t table to determine the appropriate t-table value for 95-percent confidence. 95-percent confidence corresponds to a .025 tail probability on each side of the related t distribution. Note that this value, $t = 2.447$, is larger than the t value we calculated for the original array when we had nine degrees of freedom.

5. Calculate the scale factor for the air field location (pink, green, and white helicopters) and the scale factor for our days-of-the-week blocks. By observing the data array you can recall that there are four observations in each column and three observations in each block row.

Air field helicopter

$$\text{Scale} = \frac{s}{\sqrt{4}} = \frac{.08865}{2} = .04432$$

Days of the week

$$\text{Scale} = \frac{s}{\sqrt{3}} = \frac{.08865}{1.73205} = .05118$$

Table 5.11. Adjusted residuals r^2 for days-of-the-week blocks.

Monday	.00871	.01480	.0008	
Tuesday	.00160	.00065	.000225	
Wednesday	.00640	.007225	.000025	
Thursday	.00284	.003803	.000069	
Total	.01955	.02648	.00112	

6. Calculate the two reference intervals. The product of the *t*-table value is multiplied by 2 because the interval length goes in both directions from the theoretical center point η.

Airfields

95% confidence interval length = η ± (2.447 × .04432)
= (2)(.10845) = .21690

Days of week

η ± (2.447 × .05118) = (2)(.12524) = .25048

7. Plot the intervals on the dot plots to determine if the interval stretches across all the data points. See Figures 5.8 and 5.9.

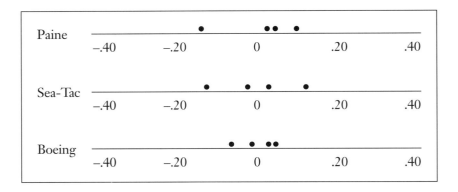

Figure 5.8. Flight time residual plots for air field location blocks, different helicopters. The airfield block intervals cover all the points.

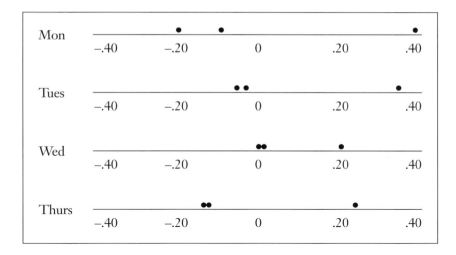

Figure 5.9. Flight time residual plots for days-of-the-week blocks. The days-of-the-week block intervals do not stretch far enough to cover all of the data points. Something is different.

Using Normal Probability Paper

Normal probability paper is an excellent tool for plotting distributions. Good computer programs graph normal probability plots or half-normal probability plots for you. Half-normal probability plots "fold the normal curve over" at the center line, so only positive values are graphed. Any data point that falls way off the straight line can be a suspected outlier.

Observations are rank ordered from small to large. The sample in Figure 5.10 graphs 15 values taken from a quincunx experiment. The fifteenth observation, with a value 18, is the outlier. I moved the funnel at the top of the quincunx to generate this outlier. A blank form, Figure 5.11, is included for practice with a quincunx.

Original data sequence:
　　　9, 14, 10, 11, 12, 13, 9, 9, 10, 12, 13, 12, 9, 18, 10

Data ordered for normal probability plot:
　　　9, 9, 9, 10, 10, 10, 11, 12, 12, 12, 13, 13, 13, 14, 18

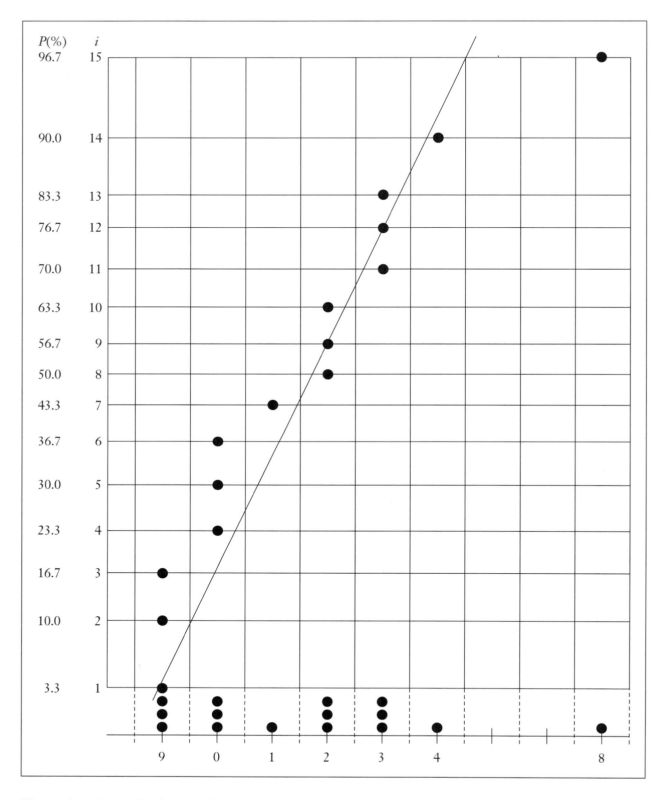

Figure 5.10. Example of a normal probability plot. The outlier value of 18 falls far off the line.

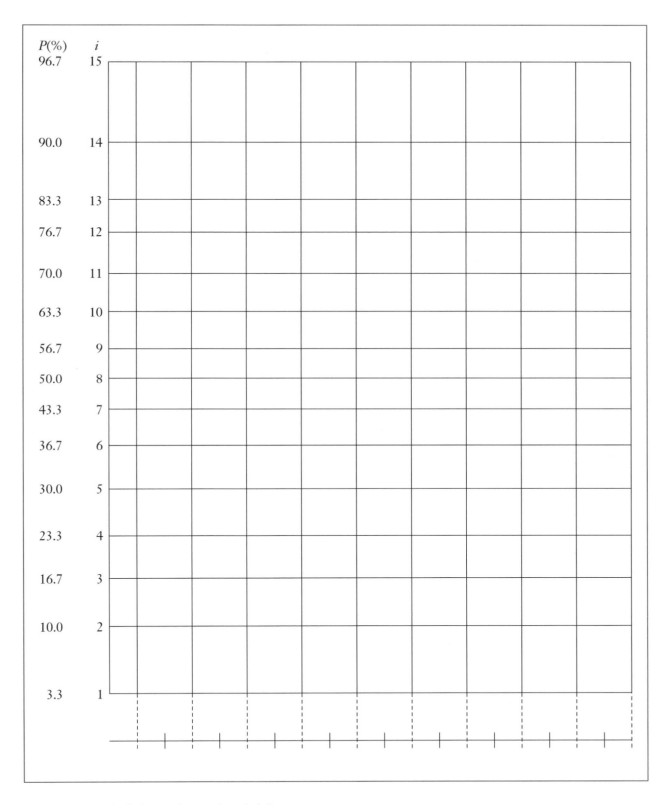

Figure 5.11. Blank sheet of normal probability paper.

An Introduction to Factorial Experiments

The best time to design an experiment is after it is finished. The worst time is at the beginning when the least is known.

—Box, Hunter, and Hunter

LEARNING OBJECTIVES

1. Students will reinforce their learning by repeating the fundamentals of data analysis.
2. Students will learn to transfer their learning with an introduction to factorial experiments.
3. Students will see practical application examples for factorial experiments in the health care sciences.
4. Students will be able to use K'NEX® toys to build an experimental design model. They will be able to use this model to describe two-factor interactions and three-factor interactions.

FACTORIAL EXPERIMENTS

Trial-and-error learning makes the sequential and iterative acquisition of knowledge an expensive proposition. The platitude, "If you think an education is expensive, try ignorance," is accurate. Choosing between a trial-and-error patient treatment plan or a directed experimentation treatment plan is an ethics puzzle that educated caregivers can solve.

Simplicity, economy, and validity are factorial experiment benefits. Categorically speaking, daily life experiences structure a continuous experiment. Main factors are varied constantly and simultaneously at different levels. The scientific method and quality control statistical method can help us learn and discover more efficiently. With science and statistical method we can apply what we learn more effectively.

DoE makes main effects, two-factor interactions, and three-factor interactions understandable. DoE lets us replace some of our hunches with knowledge. It lets us free our imaginations from guessing, so that we can focus on creative and constructive solutions. We can use our knowledge and imagination to produce the results we want when we want them. DoE gives the caregiver a tool to ensure that the patient gets just what she or he needs, just when it is needed, so that the best patient outcome is produced.

The wider inductive basis of factorial experimentation allows the caregiving team to systematically, statistically, and geometrically consider the outcome of prior-treatment outcomes. This knowledge can be generalized to a certain extent to other similar patient populations. Tables 6.1 and 6.2 arrays three variables: physician, amount of contrast media used, and gender. Each variable is set at two different levels.

DoE software identifies the standard order, randomizes the experiment order, and creates the base array. Note that the y and x columns have been switched. There is nothing sacred about the order of the three variables.

Table 6.1. Factorial experimental design for testing three factors in eight runs.

Standard order	Random order	Physician y	Contrast media x	Gender z	Fluoroscopy time
1	1	Named	≤100	Female	1.7
2	3	Named	≥101	Female	2.4
3	8	Other	≤100	Female	4.7
4	7	Other	≥101	Female	3.4
5	2	Named	≤100	Male	1.9
6	5	Named	≥101	Male	20
7	6	Other	≤100	Male	.4
8	4	Other	≥101	Male	26.1
Each line in the table represents one run. Each factor is set at two levels. This is a 2^3 design.					

Table 6.2. Factorial experimental design for testing three clinical factors in eight runs, orthogonal symbols only.

Standard order and cube number system	Physician	Contrast media	Gender	Any product resulting from factor multiplication across the row
1	−1	−1	−1	−1
2	−1	+1	−1	+1
3	+1	−1	−1	+1
4	+1	+1	−1	−1
5	−1	−1	+1	+1
6	−1	+1	+1	−1
7	+1	−1	+1	−1
8	+1	+1	+1	+1
				$\Sigma = 0$

With only a few keystrokes, you can be sure you have the most efficient orthogonal array of the main factors (see Figure 6.1). More often than not, people just use paper, pencil, and the memorized template permutation for 2^3 experiment for screening variables. (Experience shows that this array is easily memorized.) The coded data in the array in Figure 6.2 confirm the structural integrity of our design. Each result from each experiment, fluoroscopy time, can be placed on its related corner of an experimental cube. Standard order also provides the numbering system for the experimental cube.

Contrast media effect

$$2.4 - 1.7 = .7$$
$$3.4 - 4.7 = -1.30$$
$$20 - 1.9 = 18.1$$
$$26.1 - .4 = 25.7$$
$$\text{Average} = 10.8$$

The main effect is the difference between the two averages of the opposing planes, $\bar{y}_+ - \bar{y}_-$. Figure 6.3. illustrates the planes for

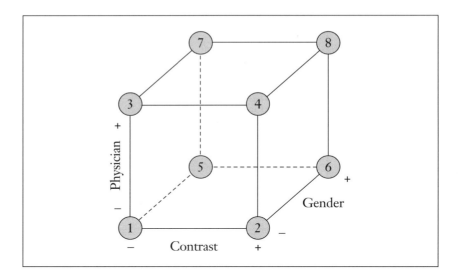

Figure 6.1. An orthogonal array frames the experimental space. Sequential experimentation is a strategy for efficient discovery.

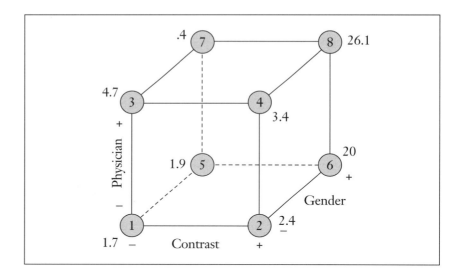

Figure 6.2. Each side of the cube is a smooth plane. The cube lets us calculate main factor effects, two-factor interactions, and three-factor interactions using addition, subtraction, multiplication, and division. Again, personal computing software does all this handwork for us so that we have time to improve quality.

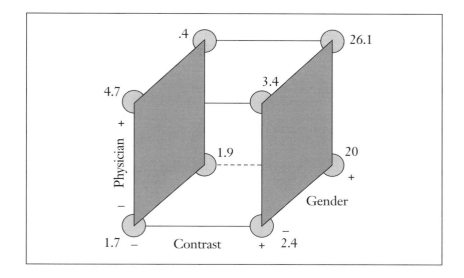

Figure 6.3. The two contrasting planes for contrast media are shaded. Coding symbols (–, +) and experimental run values are appropriately placed. Test your memory of the standard cube numbering system.

x set negative and *x* set positive. The equations for the effect for the contrast, physician, and gender factors are

$$C = \frac{2.4 + 3.4 + 26.1 + 20}{4} - \frac{1.7 + 4.7 + .4 + 1.9}{4} = 10.8$$

$$P = \frac{4.7 + .4 + 26.1 + 3.4}{4} - \frac{1.7 + 1.9 + 20 + 2.4}{4} = 2.15$$

$$G = \frac{1.9 + .4 + 26.1 + 20}{4} - \frac{2.4 + 1.7 + 4.7 + 3.4}{4} = 9.05$$

Interaction effects for two factors—for example, contrast media and gender—help us infer whether the effect of the contrast media depends on the effect of gender. See Table 6.3. The interaction effects between contrast and physician, and physician and gender, are calculated in the same manner. Higher-order, three-factor interactions calculate the difference in results when two-factor interactions are set with the third factor at plus and minus. See Figure 6.4.

The K'NEX® toy model can help us visualize the different planes created by two-factor interactions and the tetrahedrons

Table 6.3. Contrast and gender interaction effect.

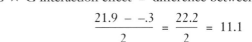

2.4 − 1.7 = .7	(−1.3 + .7) ÷ 2 = −.3
3.4 − 4.7 = −1.30	Average effect of contrast: females
20 − 1.9 = 18.1	(18.1 + 25.7) ÷ 2 = 21.9
26.1 − .4 = 25.7	Average effect of contrast: males
C × G interaction effect = difference between + and − settings	
$\dfrac{21.9 - -.3}{2} = \dfrac{22.2}{2} = 11.1$	

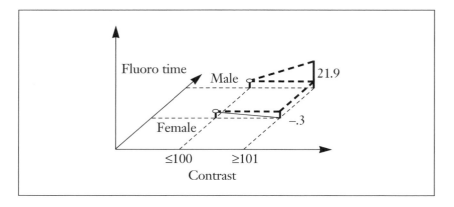

Figure 6.4. The data and graphic illustration suggest a strong interaction between the amount of contrast media used and patient gender. The variation in the fall of the front plane vector, −.3, and the rise of the back plane vector, 21.9, illustrates an interaction effect. Parallel vectors would have indicated no interaction on an interaction plot. Imagine two corresponding right triangles. If there were no effects, these two right triangles would have identical angles and identical slopes.

(3-D triangles) created by three-factor interactions. (There are four points in each tetrahedron.)

The formula for the contrast × physician interaction (C × P) is

$$C \times P = \frac{1 + 4 + 5 + 8}{4} - \frac{2 + 3 + 6 + 7}{4}$$

$$= \frac{1.7 + 3.4 + 1.9 + 26.1}{4} - \frac{2.4 + 4.7 + 20 + .4}{4}$$

$$= \frac{33.1}{4} - \frac{27.5}{4} = 8.275 - 6.875 = 1.4$$

The formula for the physician and patient gender interaction $(P \times G)$ shows an insignificant effect.

$$P \times G = \frac{1 + 2 + 7 + 8}{4} - \frac{3 + 4 + 5 + 6}{4}$$

$$= \frac{1.7 + 2.4 + .4 + 26.1}{4} - \frac{4.7 + 3.4 + 1.9 + 20}{4}$$

$$= \frac{30.6}{4} - \frac{30}{4} = 7.65 - 7.5 = 0.15$$

The formula for the three-factor interaction, contrast × physician × gender $(C \times P \times G)$, is the difference between the four points in the cube's internal, contrasting tetrahedrons. See Figure 6.5.

$$C \times P \times G$$

$$= \frac{2 + 5 + 3 + 8}{4} - \frac{1 + 6 + 7 + 4}{4}$$

$$= \frac{2.4 + 1.9 + 4.7 + 26.1}{4} - \frac{1.7 + 20 + .4 + 3.4}{4}$$

$$= 8.775 - 6.375 = 2.4$$

Figure 6.5. K'NEX® tetrahedron representing the three-factor interaction. Occasionally three-factor interactions prove to be important in daily experimentation.

Typically, main effects tend to be larger than two-factor interactions. Two-factor interactions tend to be larger than three-factor, higher-order interactions. Our upcoming case study illustrates the general rule and the exception. In practice, functions tend to be fairly smooth. Response functions tend to be similar.[1]

CASE STUDY FEATURING A TWO-FACTOR INTERACTION

The computer-generated statistical pictures for this experiment were produced with Quality America's DOE-IV software application. The application's cube numbering system differs from the standard presented in this guide. Quality America uses the letters *a, b, c, d, e, f, g,* and *h* instead of numbers 1–8. The configuration of the planes differs, but the message is identical.

Key points to remember in this experiment follow.

- The longest fluoroscopy times were observed when the patient was a male and the amount of contrast media used was 101 and greater. Differences in who the physician was did not surface as a significant factor. It is important to remember that the original hypothesis was that the physician was the "known" main factor that caused long fluoroscopy times. See Figure 6.6.

- The half-normal probability plot suggests that the two-factor interaction of patient gender and the volume of contrast media used is most significant, followed by contrast media volume and patient gender. See Figure 6.7.

- The box-and-whisker plots illustrate the remarkable differences in variability related to patient gender and contrast media volume used. Box-and-whisker plots graph the mean or median of the data sets framed in a box that represents the middle two quartiles of the distribution. The end of the whiskers, top and bottom, represent 3σ above and below the distribution center point. See Figures 6.8 and 6.9.

- The parallel lines on the physician/patient gender interaction chart suggest that these two factors do not interact. The intersecting lines on the patient sex and contrast media volume graph confirm the presence of a two-factor interaction during the experiment. See Figures 6.10 and 6.11.

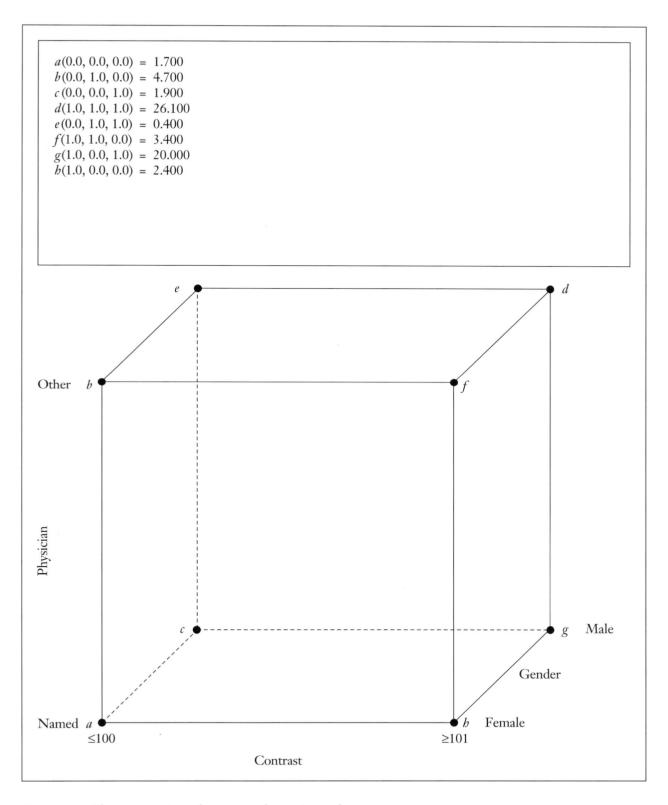

$a(0.0, 0.0, 0.0) = 1.700$
$b(0.0, 1.0, 0.0) = 4.700$
$c(0.0, 0.0, 1.0) = 1.900$
$d(1.0, 1.0, 1.0) = 26.100$
$e(0.0, 1.0, 1.0) = 0.400$
$f(1.0, 1.0, 0.0) = 3.400$
$g(1.0, 0.0, 1.0) = 20.000$
$h(1.0, 0.0, 0.0) = 2.400$

Figure 6.6. Fluoroscopy time: the measured experimental response.

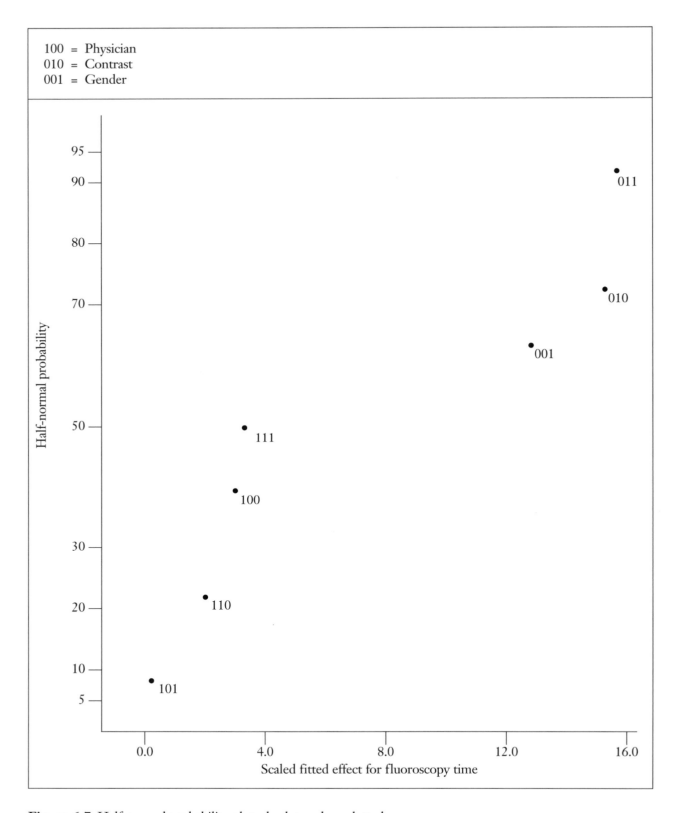

Figure 6.7. Half-normal probability plot: absolute values plotted.

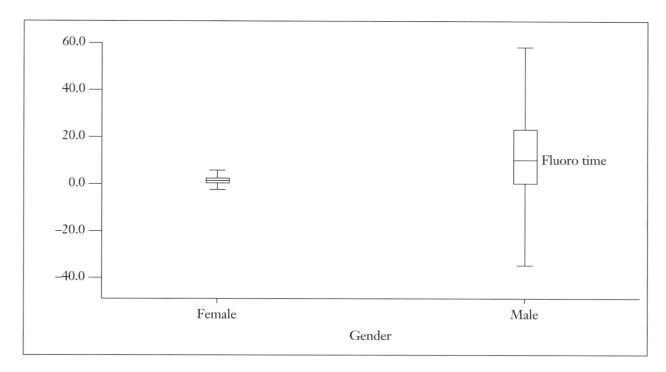

Figure 6.8. Box-and-whisker plot graphs dispersion for gender.

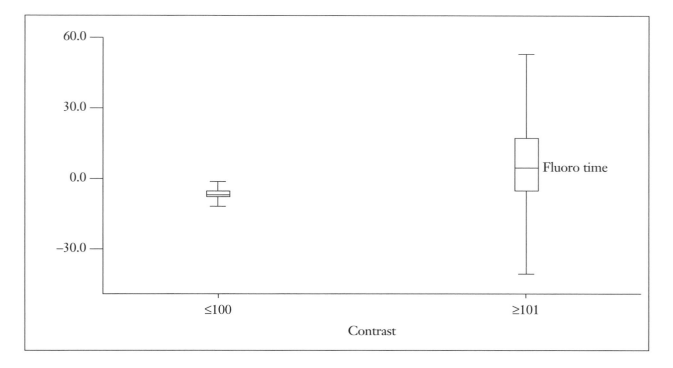

Figure 6.9. Box-and-whisker plot graphs dispersion for contrast.

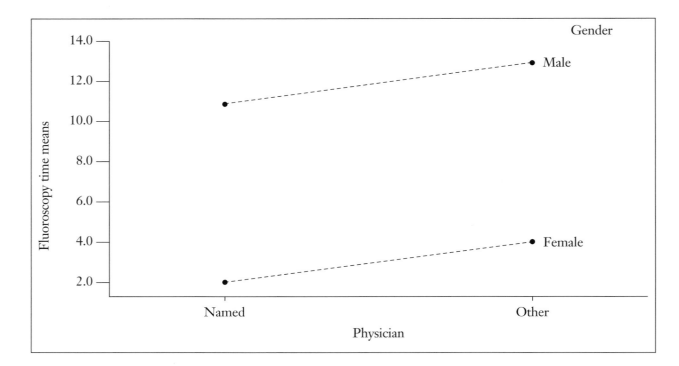

Figure 6.10. Interaction plot illustrates no interaction. Parallel lines mean similar responses at both levels.

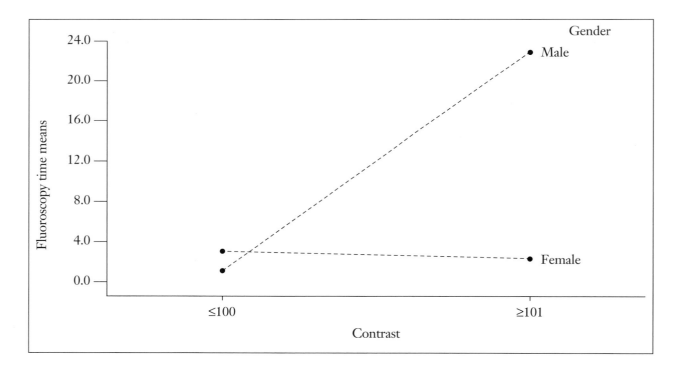

Figure 6.11. Interaction chart illustrates different responses.

There are significant variations in the quality software DoE programs. Buyers beware! Not all statistical software programs provide accurate and complete analysis features. For theoretical, analytic, and practical reasons, I recommend that Taguchi designs be studiously avoided at all times and under all circumstances. Although I admire this quality leader's articulation of certain quality philosophy ideals, I have found his reasoning to be inadequate for producing reliable, rapid improvements.

CASE STUDY FEATURING A 2^5 EXPERIMENT

Factorial experiments can be used to simultaneously evaluate any number of main effects and interactions. Each additional factor increases the required numbers of experimental runs geometrically.

This example shows a few selected statistical pictures for a 2^5 experiment. Days in accounts receivable are a function of many factors including payer type, the number of patient visits, the number of disciplines, the patient's length of stay, and the case manager. See Table 6.4. The cube, half-normal, or normal probability plots; box-and-whisker graphs; and interaction plots are all helpful in daily decision making.

- The cube illustrates that the longest number of days a bill spent in accounts receivable was observed on the top plane, risk Medicare patients. See Figure 6.12.

Table 6.4. Factors in the 2^5 example.

Label	Type		Levels
Payer type	Main factor Medicare Risk Medicare	2	Qualitative
Number of visits	Main factor 9 and below; 10+	2	Qualitative
Disciplines	Main factor 2 and below; 3+	2	Qualitative
Length of stay	Main factor 30–; 31+	2	Qualitative
Case manager	Main factor RN; PT	2	Qualitative
Days in accounts receivable	Response		

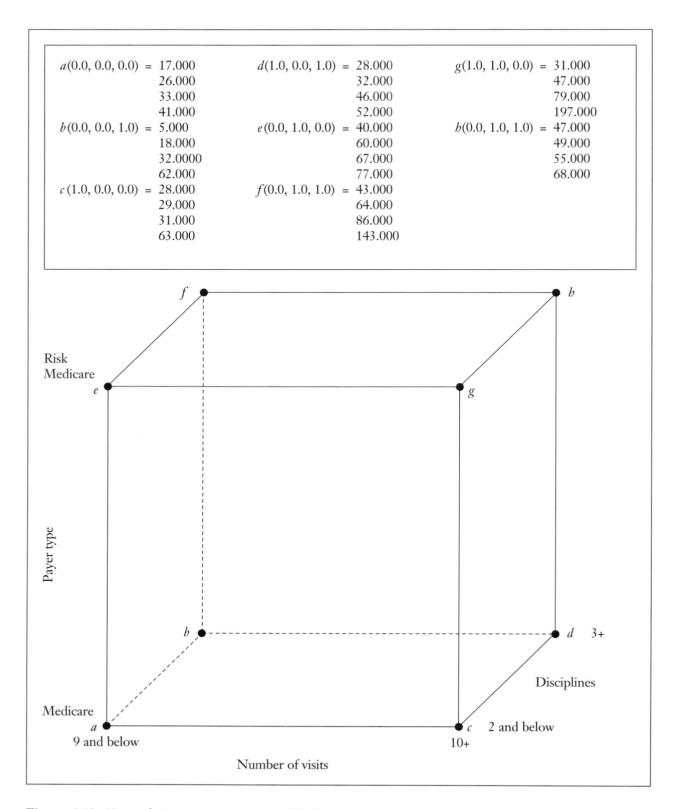

Figure 6.12. 32-run design on accounts receivable days. Four observation values are shown at each corner.

- The box-and-whisker plot illustrates days in accounts receivable variations. In this context, Medicare uses electronic billing and risk Medicare uses a handwork billing process. Electronic data transfers can have a favorable effect on cash flow! See Figure 6.13.

- The half-normal probability plot suggests that several different process factors influence the number of days in accounts receivable. Again, the payer type is the most significant outlier. See Figure 6.14.

- The two-factor interaction, case manager and number of home visits, is the kind of interesting DoE information that, in the short term, nothing can be done about. Registered nurses (RNs) manage more complex cases than physical therapists (PTs) so, consequently, it may take more time to collect a payment for services rendered. See Figure 6.15.

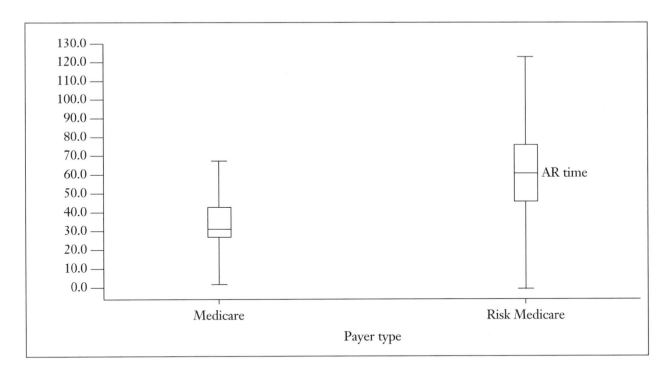

Figure 6.13. Electronic billing speed collections.

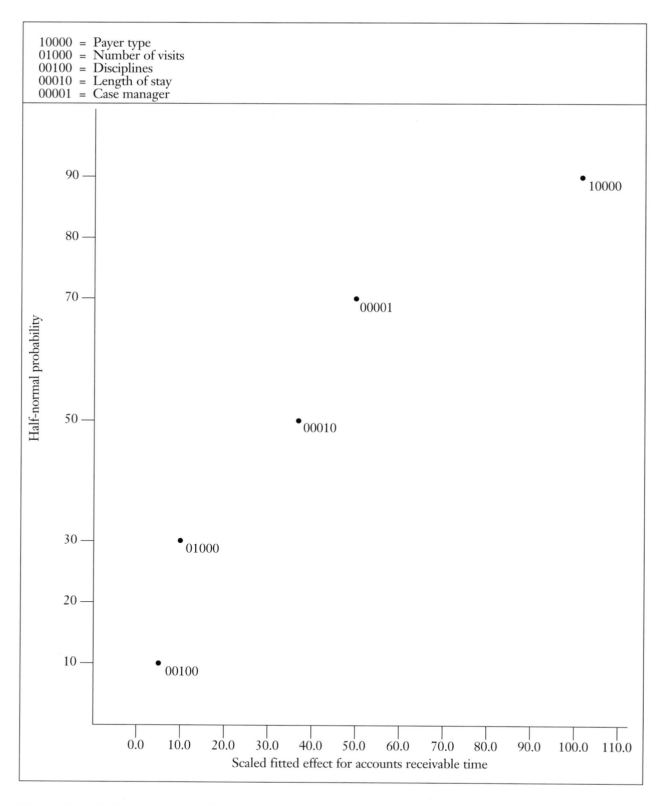

Figure 6.14. Half-normal probability plot.

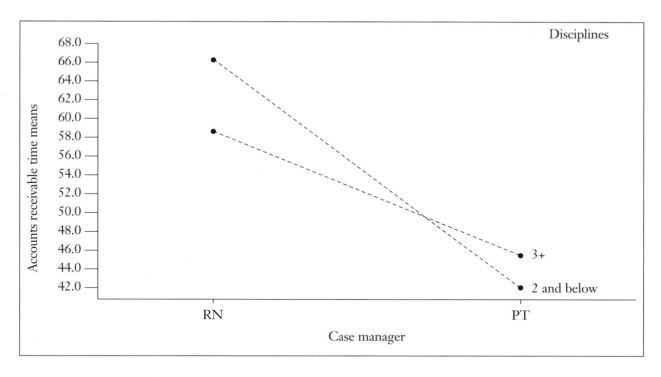

Figure 6.15. Registered nurse care managers tend to manage more complicated cases with longer accounts receivable times.

Once a series of designed experiments identifies main effects, it is up to the leadership team to act on the information. Taking action to improve the quality of clinical decisions on a case-by-case basis is the most powerful way to reduce the total costs of care because, to repeat the central point of this book, clinical judgments are the primary driver for the expenditure of resources. The language of science, statistical reasoning, improves quality and lower costs simultaneously.

An Introduction to Fractional Factorial Experiments

Never spend more than 25 percent of your experimental resources on the initial experiment.

—Box, Hunter, and Hunter

LEARNING OBJECTIVES

1. Students will be introduced to the fundamentals of fractional factorial experiments.

2. Students will know how to construct 16 different paper helicopters for use in a fractional factorial experiment.

3. Students will learn one method of dealing with a missing observation value from the fast-track aerobic exercise data set.

FRACTIONAL FACTORIAL EXPERIMENTS

As the number of factors in an experiment increase, full factorial experiments become too expensive for everyday use. Fractional factorial experiments can help screen the vital few process factors from the trivial many. The Pareto effect, frequently observed in designed experimentation, helps us focus our attention.

A full two-level factorial experiment for eight variables, 2^8, equals 256 runs. A fractional factorial screening experiment for a 2^8 allows us to evaluate all eight factors with only 16 runs! The efficiencies of this cognitive strategy are staggering. It is almost impossible to believe one can learn so much so quickly from so few data points. But truth is stranger than fiction. This works. Do what works.

The geometry of the factorial experiment lets us use a distilled essence of the cube. This essence is the fractional factorial experiment. (See Figures 7.1, 7.2, and 7.3.) Simplicity and economy are the values of fractional factorial experiments. Simplicity is the key to success with fractional factorial experiments. Simplicity is a quality science core value.

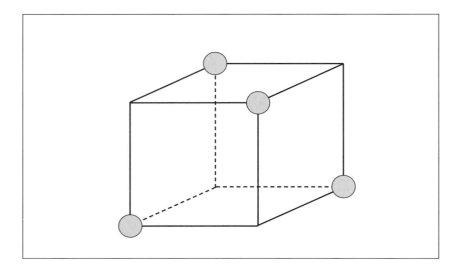

Figure 7.1. This experimental design can be projected into three 2^2 experiments.

Figure 7.2. A K'NEX® toy helps us see and hold the tetrahedron in a model cube.

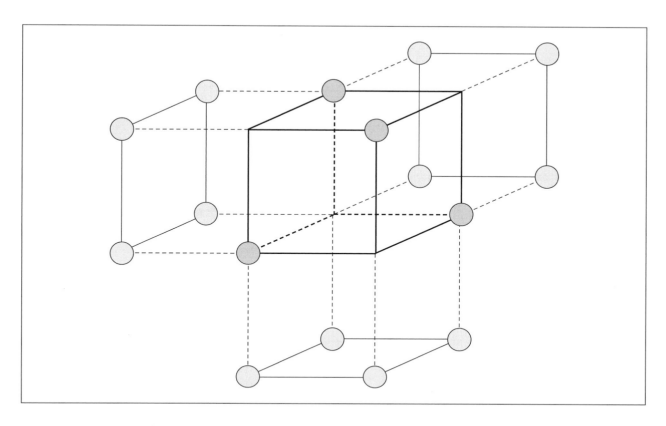

Figure 7.3. A projected 2^2 experiment.

Figure 7.1 illustrates four points of one of the tetrahedrons contained in a cube. The coordinates for the contrasting tetrahedron are the cube corner points that are not highlighted.

Experimental design, data analysis, and model building are even more enjoyable when one physically designs the experiment, analyzes the data by holding the vector representations in one's own hands, and actually builds a model. Figure 7.2 is a model constructed using K'NEX® toys and colored construction paper.

Figure 7.3 helps us visualize how the four points of three 2^2-factor experiments are created with the four tetrahedron points. Imagine that a light beam is aimed through the cube from above and from two different sides. The beam catches and projects the four highlighted points onto a wall below and two walls beside the cube. The shadow forms the square plots of three different 2^2-factor experiment designs. (Refresh your memory and review the square plot in unit 2, Gestalting Quality.)

The following orthogonal experimental data arrays provide insight to the logic of a fractional factorial design. See Table 7.1. The helicopter experiment provides the proof of the pudding that is in the eating. Fractional factorial experiments work. *Do more of what works!*

Two fractions from this array produce orthogonal fractional factorial designs: (1) runs 1, 4, 6, and 7, or, (2) runs 2, 3, 5, 8. See Table 7.2. For this reason, the three-factor interaction column for the factorial interaction is often called the *fractional factorial design generator.*

Generate the other fractional factorial design yourself in Table 7.3. Fortunately, computer programs complete all of these calculations for us automatically.

Table 7.1. Factorial experimental design: three factors at two levels.

	A	B	C	AB	AC	BC	ABC
1	−1	−1	−1	+1	+1	+1	−1
2	+1	−1	−1	−1	−1	+1	+1
3	−1	+1	−1	−1	+1	−1	+1
4	+1	+1	−1	+1	−1	−1	−1
5	−1	−1	+1	+1	−1	−1	+1
6	+1	−1	+1	−1	+1	−1	−1
7	−1	+1	+1	−1	−1	+1	−1
8	+1	+1	+1	+1	+1	+1	+1

Table 7.2. Fractional factorial design: three factors at two levels. All main factor and two-factor interaction columns sum to zero.

	A	B	C	AB	AC	BC	ABC
1	−1	−1	−1	+1	+1	+1	−1
4	+1	+1	−1	+1	−1	−1	−1
6	+1	−1	+1	−1	+1	−1	−1
7	−1	+1	+1	−1	−1	+1	−1

Table 7.3. Fractional factorial design: three factors at two levels. All main factor and two-factor interaction columns sum to zero.

	A	B	C	AB	AC	BC	ABC
2							
3							
5							
8							

CORRUGATED COPTERS EXPERIMENT

Our Corrugated Copters experiment lets us observe construction and performance variations. We can demonstrate that 16 runs are sufficient to make meaningful inferences about which of the eight factors cause a short or long flight time. See Table 7.4.

Build 16 helicopters according to the specifications in the array in Table 7.5. Pretend that each helicopter costs $1 million so that you will know how expensive poor-quality errors are. Follow the slogan "Drive down costs!" or you will go broke.

Take a moment to think categorically about these helicopters. Imagine they are patients. Some patients have wide bodies, some have thin ones. Some patients are long and some are not. Body surface area (BSA) calculations using these factors

Table 7.4. Coding arrangement for a 2^8 factorial experiment.

Factors	Code	−	+
Paper	P	Bond	Regular
Body width	B	1.25″	2.00″
Body length	L	3″	4.75″
Wing length	W	3″	4.75″
Paper clip	C	No	Yes
Fold	F	No	Yes
Body tape	BT	No	Yes
Wing tape	WT	No	Yes

Table 7.5. Orthogonal array for 16 experimental runs in a 2^8 design. Actual practice requires a randomized order of runs. For demonstration purposes, this key step is omitted.

Order	P	B	L	W	C	F	BT	WT	Flight time
1	–	–	–	–	–	–	–	–	
2	+	–	–	–	–	+	+	+	
3	–	+	–	–	+	–	+	+	
4	+	+	–	–	+	+	–	–	
5	–	–	+	–	+	+	+	–	
6	+	–	+	–	+	–	–	+	
7	–	+	+	–	–	+	–	+	
8	+	+	+	–	–	–	+	–	
9	–	–	–	+	+	+	–	+	
10	+	–	–	+	+	–	+	–	
11	–	+	–	+	–	+	+	–	
12	+	+	–	+	–	–	–	+	
13	–	–	+	+	–	–	+	+	
14	+	–	+	+	–	+	–	–	
15	–	+	+	+	+	–	–	–	
16	+	+	+	+	+	+	+	+	

have clinical significance, so the analogy is only a short imaginative reach. Some patients carry extra weight (the paper clip) low on their anatomies, and some do not. Anatomy has clinical implications. Some patients have folds, long arms, and tape, while others do not. The flight time could be the length of stay measured in days rather than seconds in the air.

Time each flight. Identify the longest flight time. Identify the shortest flight time. Without calculation you will notice longest flight times occurred with helicopters that had long wings and no paper clip attached. The shortest flights happened when the helicopter had short wings and was weighted down with a paper clip.

The wider inductive analysis you made for your sky divers transfers to helicopter flight times. The surface area of the wings and the weight of the flying object are main effects. Cosmetic appearances, color or tape, are not significant factors unless they increase the surface area or weight. If you had an unlimited amount of time and money, you could run the additional 240 experimental runs. Additional experiments, using homogeneous samples, will affirm the validity of your inductive and, in this case, intuitive inference. But the question is, can you afford the indulgence in a competitive helicopter market at this moment in time?

Fast-track experiments using catapults, paper helicopters, handkerchief sky divers, and aerobic exercise are ideal for learning. The results from these experiments confirm what we already know to be true. It is a mystery as to why we weren't all taught to use this analytic tool set in grade school. In actual practice, designed experimentation leads us to counterintuitive conclusions and significant cognitive dissonance. Helping people conquer the dissonance created by designed experiments is a life's work.

With directed experimentation, you will find scores of "cosmetic" health care management practices that add nothing but expense. If your learning curve is like mine, you will quickly discover counterproductive treatment protocols. You will uncover a plethora of ways to improve patient safety. And you will have to struggle to convince others. The IDEA cycle is not just about thinking, it is about action.

As the quality of health care improves, costs shrink only if you take action on your knowledge. Showing the personal courage to address difficult administrative and practice issues is important to success. When your resolve flags, remember how difficult it was for Florence Nightingale to persuade medical authorities to meet her unreasonable demands for clean bedding, soup, and the preposterous luxury of hospital clothing.[1]

Also recall the work of Ignaz Philipp Semmelweis. Semmelweis observed how important hand washing was to the prevention of puerperal fever. In spite of overwhelming experimental evidence, he failed to convince the experts of his time. Infection control specialists know that even today convincing caregivers to wash their hands at appropriate and frequent intervals is still a challenge.

The Fisher and Box model for efficient learning falls into the identical, revolutionary change category. If your experimental results do not immediately produce cultural transformations, know that you are in excellent company. With persistence and determination, good designs and good data, you will win over time. Stick with it even if you must work alone and on your own.

Computerized and automated statistical analysis software applications make designed experimentation affordable. We could complete a formal analysis of our flight times by hand. Since this is an introductory guide, and since I am trying to persuade you to use DoE software, Table 7.6 and Figure 7.4–7.7 show the charts a computer can produce in a few minutes using our flight times. Through these charts we see that

- One of the many cubes we can produce with our data shows that the longest flight times occurred with helicopters that had long wings and no paper clip weight.

Table 7.6. Computer-generated orthogonal array for a 2^8 helicopter experiment. Every combination is a different configuration of the eight variables. See Box, Hunter, and Hunter's text for specific instructions on designing this experiment.[2]

Run	Paper	Body width	Body length	Wing length	Clip	Fold	Body tape	Wing tape	Flight time	
1	Bond	1.25	3.00	3.00	No	No	No	No	1.54	
2	Regular	1.25	3.00	3.00	No	Yes	Yes	Yes	1.46	
3	Bond	2.00	3.00	3.00	Yes	No	Yes	Yes	1.12	→ Shortest flight
4	Regular	2.00	3.00	3.00	Yes	Yes	No	No	1.14	= short wings +
5	Bond	1.25	4.75	3.00	Yes	Yes	Yes	No	1.15	paper clip
6	Regular	1.25	4.75	3.00	Yes	No	No	Yes	1.18	
7	Bond	2.00	4.75	3.00	No	Yes	No	Yes	1.35	
8	Regular	2.00	4.75	3.00	No	No	No	No	1.56	
9	Bond	1.25	3.00	4.75	Yes	Yes	No	Yes	2.09	
10	Regular	1.25	3.00	4.75	Yes	No	Yes	No	2.10	
11	Bond	2.00	3.00	4.75	No	Yes	Yes	No	2.53	→ Longest flight
12	Regular	2.00	3.00	4.75	No	No	No	Yes	2.48	= long wings +
13	Bond	1.25	4.75	4.75	No	No	Yes	Yes	2.47	no paper clip
14	Regular	1.25	4.75	4.75	No	Yes	No	No	2.48	
15	Bond	2.00	4.75	4.75	Yes	No	No	No	2.05	
16	Regular	2.00	4.75	4.75	Yes	Yes	Yes	Yes	2.18	

The geometry of the design allows us to make a correct visual inspection!

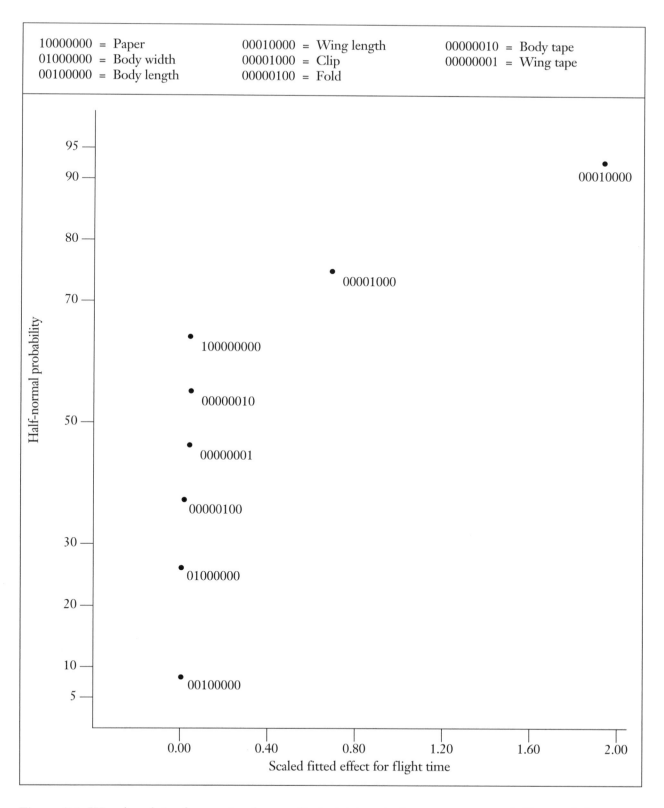

Figure 7.4. Wing length (surface area) and paper clip (weight): main factors pop out on a half-normal plot.

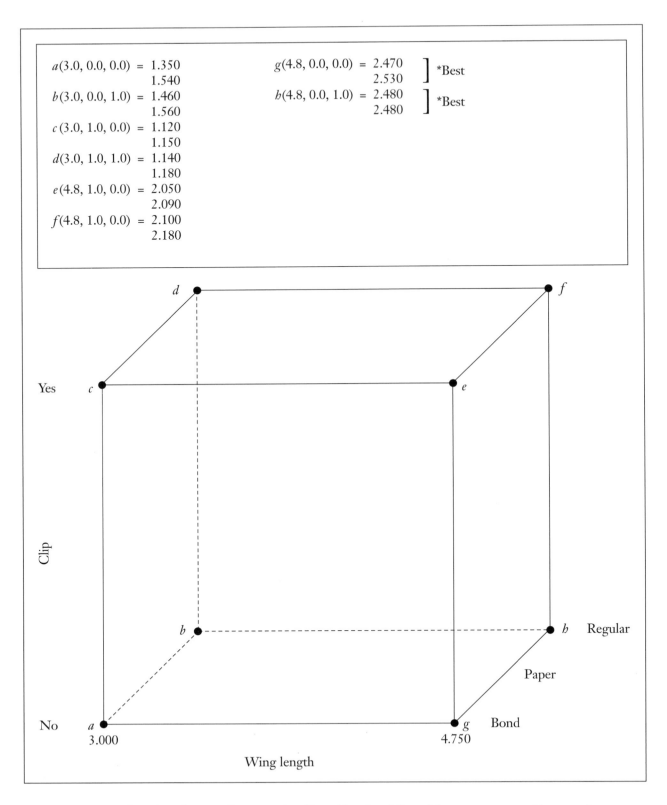

$a(3.0, 0.0, 0.0) = 1.350$
$\qquad 1.540$
$b(3.0, 0.0, 1.0) = 1.460$
$\qquad 1.560$
$c(3.0, 1.0, 0.0) = 1.120$
$\qquad 1.150$
$d(3.0, 1.0, 1.0) = 1.140$
$\qquad 1.180$
$e(4.8, 1.0, 0.0) = 2.050$
$\qquad 2.090$
$f(4.8, 1.0, 0.0) = 2.100$
$\qquad 2.180$

$g(4.8, 0.0, 0.0) = 2.470$] *Best
$\qquad 2.530$
$h(4.8, 0.0, 1.0) = 2.480$] *Best
$\qquad 2.480$

Figure 7.5. Wing length and paper clip are main effects. Fractional factorials are accurate and inexpensive.

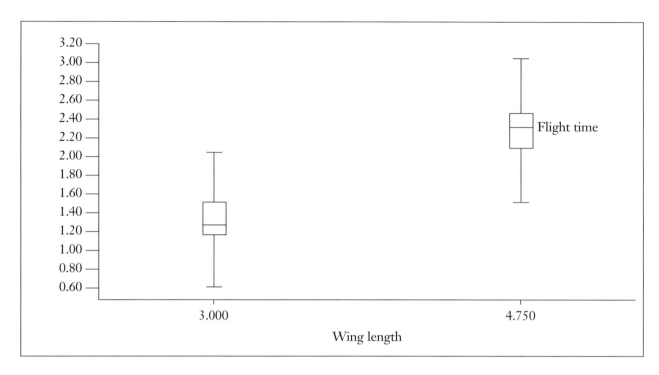

Figure 7.6. Long wings cause longer flights. Helicopter color is irrelevant.

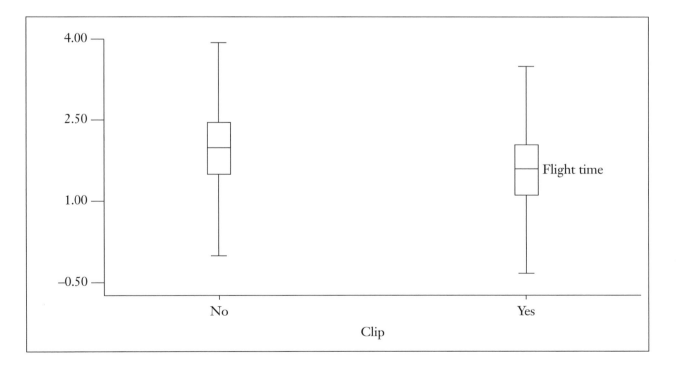

Figure 7.7. Clip is less influential, unless the clip is heavy.

- The half-normal probability plot confirms our intuitive analysis that wing length and paper clip are main factors. The plot suggests no other main factors or interaction are present.
- The box-and-whisker plots comparing the flight times of helicopters with long wings and those with short wings makes our decisions easier.

Calculation and quantification are critically important to the credibility of your data presentations. It is important for experimenters to demonstrate a personal discipline to the theory and principles of designed experimentation. Intuition and personal perception are insufficient for making well-reasoned decisions.

Remember that the Pythagoras, Decartes, Fisher, and Box mathematical model holds true in any universe. Pay close attention when the results of your experiments aren't what you hoped or knew for certain they would be. Don't be afraid to use your new knowledge to improve patient safety. There is no need to form a committee and brainstorm ideas when principles, sound theory, common sense, and expert knowledge are sufficient.

WHAT TO DO WITH A MISSING VALUE

Occasionally observations are lost, data are misplaced, or a catastrophe befalls the lead experimenter that derails the entire experiment. What does one do when faced with a missing experimental value? Algebra and geometry provide a simple way to fit, or estimate, a missing value.

In theory and in practice, the three-factor interaction in Table 7.7, labeled column ABC, is rarely significant. If we assume the three-factor interaction is inert, we can set the sum of experimental values we get from our experiment in this column equal to zero. Then we can simply solve for the missing value as in Table 7.8.

Here is how the algebra works for the aerobic exercise example in Figure 2.25 (see page 51). Multiply values in the actual heart rate column by the sign in the ABC column. An inert three-factor interaction would total zero.

Table 7.7. Factorial experimental design: three factors at two levels.

	A	B	C	AB	AC	BC	ABC
1	−1	−1	−1	+1	+1	+1	−1
2	+1	−1	−1	−1	−1	+1	+1
3	−1	+1	−1	−1	+1	−1	+1
4	+1	+1	−1	+1	−1	−1	−1
5	−1	−1	+1	+1	−1	−1	+1
6	+1	−1	+1	−1	+1	−1	−1
7	−1	+1	+1	−1	−1	+1	−1
8	+1	+1	+1	+1	+1	+1	+1

Table 7.8. Solving for the missing heart rate value. The missing value is estimated using simple algebra.

	Actual heart rate	ABC	Heart rates with missing value
Run 1	72	−	−72
Run 2	68	+	68
Run 3	80	+	80
Run 4	76	−	−76
Run 5	140	+	140
Run 6	136	−	−136
Run 7	156	−	$-x$ (missing value)
Run 8	160	+	160
			Model sum = 0 Actual sum = 164

Our estimate is not exact. 164 is 8 heartbeats more than the actual 156, yet our estimate yields a result that will produce remarkably similar results for the main effect and two-factor interactions we calculated using all the data in the original fast-track experiment. Plug the new data set into the template formulas to prove this to yourself. This is just one more example of the economy and efficiency created by designed experiments.

Section III

Success Stories

UNIT EIGHT

Success Stories

Most teachers are knowledge-able. Good teachers are intelligent. Great teachers are patient. Exceptional teachers are students themselves.

—Dale Dubin, M.D.
Rapid Interpretation of EKGs

LEARNING OBJECTIVES

1. Students will learn how a new organizational design model promotes rapid, continuous improvement.

2. Students will practice making inferences by reviewing selected statistical pictures from selected experiments.

PERSONAL QUALITIES THAT APPEAR IN SUCCESS STORIES

The personal initiative of dedicated professionals is the main factor that predicts designed experiments success stories. Professionals take pride in their work. They feel responsible for the quality of their work. Professionalism is an attitude that can be found at all levels in any organization of people. Title and position do not always indicate who is or is not a professional. Personal discipline, knowledge, industry, and character play important roles.

Industrious people just seem to believe that progress can occur. They believe work is worthwhile and that their work can make a difference. The following list of individual behaviors and qualities of character sparkle during every results-based improvement process: designed experimentation and statistical process control. Although I have outlined these personal qualities of character in other work, it is important to name them again.[1]

1. Optimism, a belief that things can and should be constantly improved. Optimists believe their work can, does, and will contribute to worthwhile improvement.

151

2. Relentless persistence and a sense of ethical imperative about the importance of quality improvement.

3. Bulldog determination.

4. A willingness to repeatedly take calculated risk.

5. Inquisitiveness and a profound commitment to the inherent value of reading, writing, using arithmetic, and continuous study.

6. Stewardship, service, and patience with people.

7. A well-developed sense of humor.

Few people willingly and knowingly question authority on a daily basis. This natural aversion to conflict is a primary obstacle you must overcome if you expect to succeed in shrinking costs. Designed experiments systematically question the roots of power and authority in the health science's community: professional knowledge and competence.[2]

Many times the courage required to question authority rises from the power that teams of dedicated people create. The convergence of ideas that the cube creates builds teamwork faster than any process I have ever observed. When this convergence is augmented with systematic compliments and public recognition for work well done, rapid improvement occurs overnight.

Many times the individual must stand alone with only his or her principles for support. Designed experimentation takes personal courage. Not infrequently, designed experiments expose faulty reasoning at every organizational level. Like it or not, the skilled experimenter will one day find himself or herself at odds with clinical, operational, and financial bureaucrats who favor guesswork over brainwork.

QUALITY: THE PHILOSOPHY OF APPLIED LOGIC AND DEMOCRATIC PRINCIPLE

Aristotle correctly taught his students that induction must precede deduction. The discipline of inductive analytic reasoning, mathematical reasoning, requires us to count, measure, and draw pictures of data over time. Graphing our empirical observations in their original sequence leads to high-quality inferences. Shewhart's control chart, Galton's scatter diagram and regression analysis, Fisher's experimental cube, and Box's cube extensions are the best tools for plotting data over time. Personal computers eliminate hand calculations. Computers put high-level logic within everyone's reach so that the logic can be applied.

Pythagoras, Francis Bacon, Hume, Immanuel Kant, Einstein, Fisher, Shewhart, Deming, Box, and a host of other quality science luminaries have repeatedly demonstrated the wisdom in Aristotle's counsel. In our work, we call the inductive-deductive reasoning process the IDEA cycle: induction, deduction, evaluation, and action. For 2300 years the IDEA cycle, by any name, has been and remains the foundation for the scientific method, continuous improvement, the quality control chart, and the designed experiment. See Figure 8.1.

Aristotle's books *Posterior Analytics* and *Eudemian Ethics* are the original sources for all 14 of Deming's points, the Deming/Shewhart improvement cycle, Deming's profound knowledge, and the twentieth century's definition of statistical reasoning.

One essence of the Aristotle, Shewhart, and Deming argument is that going to work provides no excuse for a retreat from the principles of scientific reasoning and democratic principle. Rather, the process of going to work affords the single best

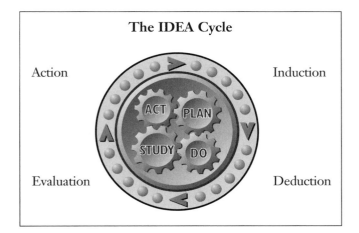

Figure 8.1. Aristotle's cycle of induction/deduction is the foundation for the scientific method. When used in the continuous improvement of health care services, the IDEA cycle causes rapid quality improvements and rapid cost reductions.

opportunity to champion quality principles. One should always treat others with trust, decency, and respect. Aristotle's model of science and democracy is pragmatic. It produces impressive results. Quality improves, and all costs—human and financial—diminish continuously. Aristotle offers an excellent organizational design solution.

SHRINKING HEALTH CARE COSTS

The process of shrinking health care costs with designed experiments has three steps.

Step1: Imagine Bold Improvement

Envisioning rapid, continuous improvement is essential. Once you and your colleagues imagine improvement, you must develop the technical competency and knowledge required to make your vision come true. The adage, ambition without education is like a boat without water, is true for the quality sciences. This book is proof that with a few good teachers, a couple of good textbooks, and practice, a person can learn to do designed experiments through self-study.

Step 2: Replace Bureaucratic Pyramids with Self-Governing Systems

Too many quality improvement leaders champion bureaucracy. Deming and Juran specifically recommend it. This has not been helpful advice. Bureaucracy increases costs! It slows improvement to a crawl.

Since 1925 the Prussian management model—bureaucracy—has used a pyramid as is its model for organization. As Figure 8.2 illustrates, this model is an obstacle to rapid improvement. People have to go through layers of brick and mortar to work efficiently. Laborious project chartering processes, affinity diagrams, fishbone diagrams of confusion, and flow diagrams that institutionalize minutia are classic examples of bureaucratic bricks and mortar.

The molecular organization model in Figure 8.3 provides a visual image of a dynamic and flexible organization. The model suggests energy and the efficient organization of a self-governing system, social hierarchy. Teams can bond with each other as

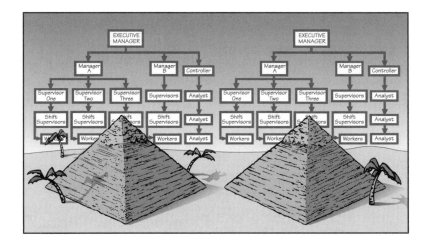

Figure 8.2. Bureaucratic pyramids slow quality improvement to a crawl.

quickly as needed to deliver high-quality services and lower total costs. Open communication accelerates quality improvement and cost reduction.

Bureaucracies are closed systems. Information is tightly controlled and closed off from the people in the system who work. Physics teaches us that closed systems create entropy and chaos. Bureaucracies are incompatible with rapid improvement.

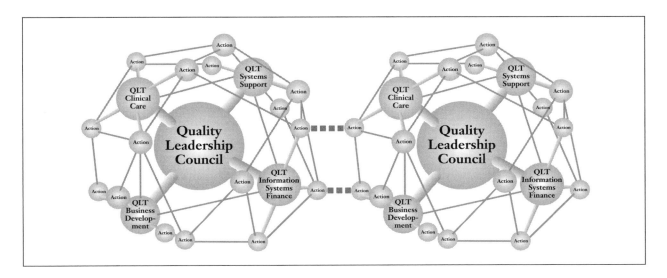

Figure 8.3. A molecular organization moves fast. Applied logic and democratic principle help the organization adapt quickly to changing conditions.

The molecular organizational design model, the model of biology, is an open system that creates an opportunity for maximum organization: negative entropy and order. Statistical methods from the viewpoint of quality control and the geometry in designed experimentation enrich the information. The precision and accuracy these tools add to communication lead to a convergence of opinion about what the truth of a given process is. Convergence causes quality improvement action in an open system where high-quality information travels reliably and quickly to everyone in the system.

A Molecule Works Better Than a Pyramid. A dynamic social system "where high quality information travels reliably and quickly to everyone in the system" sounds too good to be true. Fortunately, the claim is valid in a molecular organization where the language of applied logic, statistical reasoning, and democratic principles are core values.

In a bureaucracy, the weight and importance of one person's opinion are based on title, that person's position in the scalar chain of command, the power bestowed through a personal appointment, or all three. Rarely, if ever, do bureaucratic executives, vice presidents, managers, or staff people turn to line personnel for advice, counsel, or an advanced statistical analysis.

A society that is graduating millions of computer literate and statistically informed students from its high schools and colleges will soon grow intolerant of bureaucratic administrators who eschew computers and deny the statistical organization of our universe. Young graduates entering the workforce justifiably expect to use their knowledge. Only a poor manager would decline opportunities to apply the expert subject matter knowledge that people bring to work with them. Knowledge, analytic ability, and competence are increasingly valuable in an information-based economy. At all levels, health care is an information industry. Information increases in value as the quality of judgment improves. The scientific method, inductive analytic reasoning, improves judgment.

The molecule produces success stories—improved judgments and decisions that shrink costs—because the language of the molecular organization is the language of practical, applied science. Bureaucracies fail to produce rapid quality improvements or lower costs because the mindset created by the language of bureaucracy is more often than not a series of by-guess-and-by-golly bar graphs.

Unit 1 included an example of lucky-guess bar graphing. Another example, a four-year cost accounting bar graph trend analysis, illustrates how easily bar graph sophistry can backfire on an unwitting organization. Table 8.1 summarizes four years of financial data. Department revenue could just as well be expense. It could be supply costs or other measures.

A chart wizard on a spreadsheet application will thoughtlessly produce a bar graph, as in Figure 8.4. The wizard will embellish the chart with a linear trend line. I have been in the room when a CEO has used such a graph to substantiate his report that, "The $307,749 dollar growth in revenue represents a 5 percent improvement over our past performance. This trend shows my management team has achieved its goals."

Balderdash and poppycock? Yes. But I have also watched as the board of directors for a $100 million health care institution nodded their approval as this yarn was spun. I have seen the quality and safety of patient safety be compromised by this kind

Table 8.1. Departmental revenue summary example.

	1991	1992	1993	1994
January	404,400	525,888	489,336	527,122
February	379,001	483,776	505,696	498,000
March	434,900	501,445	535,889	509,454
April	470,850	476,900	460,332	535,677
May	520,118	544,988	501,334	464,878
June	527,030	483,443	496,887	504,444
July	461,110	450,225	542,190	477,899
August	490,324	497,003	482,307	527,334
September	494,555	555,798	514,221	490,434
October	498,884	542,330	452,254	498,554
November	540,985	497,234	483,543	515,345
December	509,000	450,334	449,996	489,765
Total	5,731,157	6,009,364	5,913,985	6,038,906

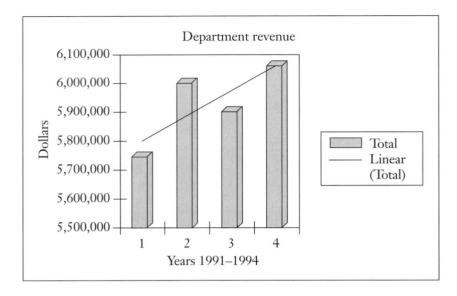

Figure 8.4. A classic example of a bar graph blunder.

of fabrication. I have observed the bar graph decision-making phenomenon in hundreds of organizations in dozens of states and overseas. The costs of poor-quality analyses are incalculable.

By clicking the mouse button, a better-informed and statistically literate leader will take 10 seconds to complete a one-way ANOVA. The results in Table 8.2 are unequivocal. There is no

Table 8.2. A single-factor ANOVA study on four years' worth of data.

Summary					
Groups	Count	Sum	Average	Variance	Standard deviation
1991	12	5731157	477596.4	2.49E+09	49888.86
1992	12	6009364	500780.3	1.24E+09	35195.55
1993	12	5913985	492832.1	8.86E+08	29770.1
1994	12	6038906	503242.2	4.45E+08	21102.39
ANOVA					

Source of variation	SS	df	MS	F	P value	F crit
Between groups	4814787481	3	1.6E+09	1.26892	0.296722	2.8165
Within groups	55651137592	44	1.26E+09			
Total	60465925073	47				

statistically significant difference between the four years. To the best of our reasoning and anybody else's reasoning ability in the late twentieth century, one can only say that the 5-percent difference, the observed variance, is a chance variation.

If the status quo was this CEO's goal, it has been achieved. But there is no evidence to support the contention, implied by the bar chart's trend line, that there has been growth.

Since the *F* test does not describe process stability, predictability, or the pattern of variation around the mean, the data are exported to a statistical process control software application. Since financial data are often autocorrelated, one data point forecasts the next data point, the first chart may be an autocorrelation chart. See Figure 8.5. Since none of the bars on this graph exceed the upper or lower control limits of probability, the analyst feels comfortable graphing the data on an individuals chart. See Figure 8.6.

There are only two circled special cause, improbable data points in the array. In each case, these variations were due to accounting corrections. For the purposes of this example, the analyst can say that there is no evidence of any out-of-control or trend patterns of variation.

The single best book that provides additional details and examples of statistical misrepresentation is Darrell Huff's 1954 *How to Lie with Statistics*.[3] His name for the bar graph is the gee-whiz graph. It is impossible to read Huff's description of Karl Marx's assumption and presumption, out-to-lunch economic logic and not equate it with the annual budgeting process many organizations use to predict their futures.

Quality-literate and numerate individuals understand the importance of graphed data. They want to understand. They use statistical reasoning to improve their perspective. They use honest graphs and valid analysis to promote accurate communication. They use their knowledge of the mean, standard deviation, and probability to reduce the risks associated with important judgments. In a molecular organization, confabulation and superstitious learning are never used as substitutes for critical thinking.

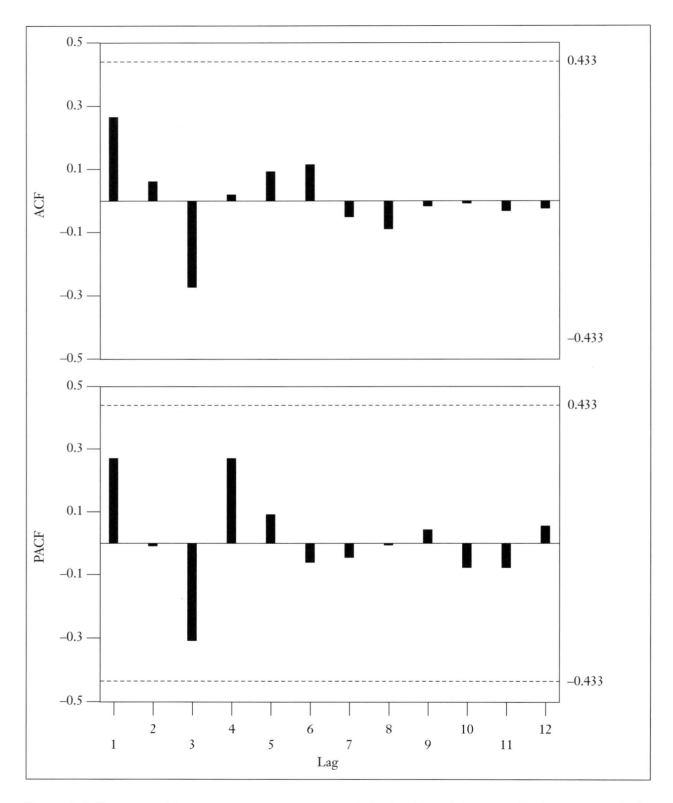

Figure 8.5. Four years of department revenue: no autocorrelation is evident. Software applications automate high-level statistical analysis.

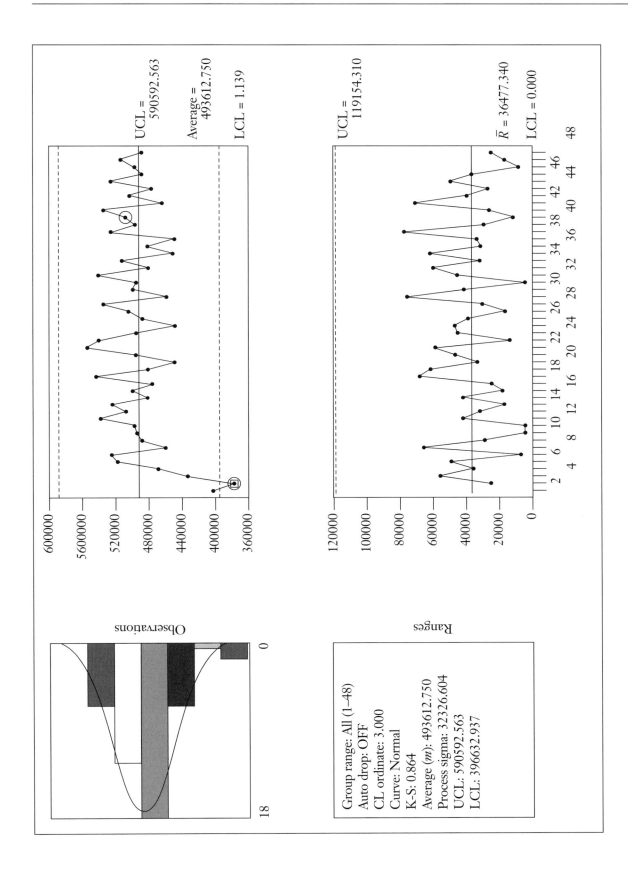

Figure 8.6. Four years of department revenue. Special cause variations are evident in quality analysis.

The Buffalo Dance and the Medicine Man. A little more than 100 years ago the plains of North America were rich with buffalo. Virtually any hunter with any weapon could bag handsome trophies. The culture that developed around this beautiful beast included a variety of rituals, beliefs, and rich dances. The power of myth prevailed. Dances were done to praise the noble beast. Dances were done to make more buffalo appear for better hunting.

Tribal power was bestowed on individuals who appeared to have an ability to create bountiful hunting grounds. Sometimes one individual could produce buffalo and he could cure the sick. This shaman came to be known as the medicine man.

The medicine man knew nothing about migratory patterns. In all probability he was not interested in learning about them. Learning that his dances were superstition may have destroyed his beliefs about who he was and how he thought his work added value to the life of his tribe. With a short-term perspective, he may have feared that teaching people and sharing knowledge was a surrender of power.

White hunters killed without conscience. An entire ecosystem was thrown off balance. As buffalo migrations dwindled toward extinction, dances were done with greater intensity. Medicine men struggled to retain power. Superstitions die slowly.

A little more than 10 years ago the North American health care system was rich with what seemed to be unlimited resources. Virtually any entrepreneur with any kind of organization could bag handsome trophies. The culture that developed around this market had a variety of rituals, beliefs, and dances.

Some enterprises profited without conscience. Competitive pressures in the health care market increased. Some organizations and the meaningful work they provided in their communities were lost forever. More organizations and the work they provide will needlessly be lost in the future. The migration of meaningful work and money is apparent to those who know how to look at and interpret patterns.

The management dances of the past are not divine. We are lucky there are still enough resources roaming around the Great Plains of North America to produce good profits. Unfortunately, short-term profitability makes it appear as though the administrative rituals of bureaucracy work. Feverous dancing continues. Dancing will not improve the systems patterns, but good judgment and improved decision quality can.

Fortunately, increasing numbers of health care industry tribal leaders are embracing the value of education. They are beginning to emphasize the importance of math and science in every curriculum. These leaders value statistical reasoning. Because they are familiar with the concept of systems thinking, they understand that the continued abuse of a precious resource can destroy an ecosystem of any size. Money and meaningful work are the resources. Ecosystem in this instance means our nation's economic system.

Today's leaders do not rely on superstitious learning; they value knowledge. They know that the process of teaching people how to improve their thinking builds power. These leaders are living up to their educational responsibilities.

They are paying employees to learn. People are learning to think for themselves. They are learning that the analytic tool set of quality improvement is a great help in lowering the costs of delivering care. They know that as the quality of their thinking improves, patients will win. Organizations will thrive. The system will cost less and it will be able to serve more people. Quality is as reliable a force as gravity is.

Step 3: Meet Your Responsibilities

In a molecular organization, team leaders and team members share responsibility and accountability for success. Self-governance entails considerable responsibility. Team leaders and team members are expected to demonstrate personal industry and initiative. A good work ethic, eloquently defined by Aristotle, is a universal expectation. Statistical reasoning skills are an expectation. Applied logic and democratic principle drive continuous, rapid improvement.

The success stories introduced in previous chapters, fluoroscopy times in the cath lab and days in accounts receivable for a home care business, are classic examples of team leaders and team members working together to gain an understanding of complex clinical and financial issues.

The original hypothesis for the fluoroscopy time study was that the main factor would be the practice patterns of given physicians. Everyone knew this was true. The reason we did the study was because this fact was true. The designed experiment model would confirm our knowledge. It would be a safe study that wouldn't create a disturbance.

True to form, our first designed experiment, the fluoroscopy study, taught us that the accepted truth wasn't true at all. We learned that, systematically, men and women are treated differently in the cath lab. The questions are "Why?" and "Is there anything we can or should do about the differences?" As simple as this insight is, the implications of the answers to this question are significant. The answers can help us improve the quality of care and lower the costs of care.

The days-in-accounts-receivable study produced lots of answers. It produced even more questions. The dramatic improvements in cash flow that electronic billing produces are a lesson for any manager who still harbors the notion that a business can be run competitively without the power of personal computers.

Designed experiments are faster and less expensive than trial-and-error learning. Plus, the graphs produced—the information produced—in a designed experiment create the convergence of informed opinion that Box, Hunter, and Hunter allude to in their work. The graphs often create compelling cases for improvement that persuade even the most intransigent bureaucrat.

Operationally, the two performance expectations for work are outlined in Figure 8.7 and 8.8. Team members have the primary charge of continuously improving the dynamics of daily routine. Control charts, scatter diagrams with correlation analyses, and 2^3 experiments are used every day. Team leaders are expected to gain enough proficiency to complete their analyses independently. Leaders are expected to role model and teach the use of the quality sciences.

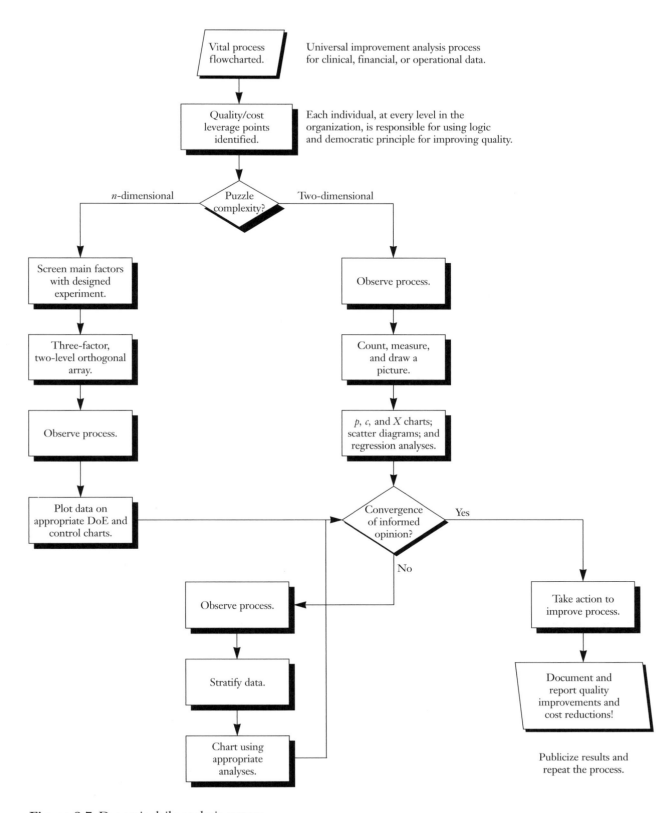

Figure 8.7. Dynamic daily analysis system.

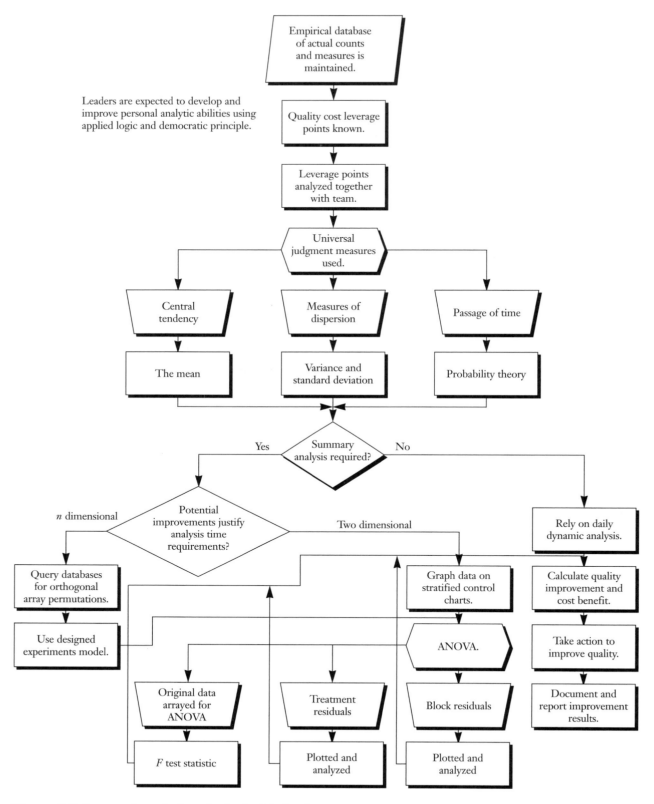

Figure 8.8. Systematic analysis at the leadership level.

Pick a process puzzle, any puzzle. Designed experiments can help you solve it. Confounding clinical, financial or operational questions can be solved through strategic questioning, experimentation, and analysis.

The following story typifies the kind of response I see from imaginative people who learn about designed experiments for the first time. Following an eight-minute DoE demonstration using the catapult and a one-hour dialogue, a receptionist pulled me aside and said, "Follow me. I want to show you three variables for an experiment." We walked down the hallway, and she shushed me with a finger to her lips. Then she pointed to an open door. Inside, three managers were arguing a point. Not one of them had data or an analysis. It was, as is too often the case, an airing of uninformed opinion. They were going nowhere fast.

We chuckled and agreed to defer this improvement project opportunity until a later date. Then we addressed one of her problems: how to improve the phone answering process.

As a receptionist, one of her many jobs was to answer the phones. A management edict required that all calls be answered under all circumstances in less than three rings. Management had conveyed the strong impression that this courtesy standard was nonnegotiable. What management was not aware of when it instituted this standard, and what the frontline team members were not able to convey, was the magnitude of a problem originally caused by a management mistake. The management system listed one of the organization's phone numbers incorrectly in every telephone directory in the state. The wrong listing could not be removed or disconnected. The phone would ring off the hook all year long.

After the fact and from a distance, the mistake and the solution seem so simple. That is this story's point. That is the point of designed experiments.

In a bureaucracy, administrators often make well-intentioned, but uninformed or underinformed policies based on personal judgment. "Unanswered phones are a problem! That incessant ringing is driving me crazy. Our customers must be outraged. I hate voice mail, and my customers won't ever get a machine when they call us."

Good intentions are not a complete foundation for good leadership. The uninformed judgment prompts the administrator to make a decision. "I'm tired of waiting for my staff to get the message. I'll fix the problem myself. From now on all phones will be answered in less than three rings." Management announces the new policy through one-way edict. There is no dialogue. No questions. Time is money and money is time. Management insists that every person obey the new rule. People are afraid to speak up.

Who wants to tell the person who signs their paychecks that a management error created the problem? Who wants to say that answering the phone in three rings won't solve it?

The process of designed experimentation got everyone around one table. Data and a data analysis created a convergence of opinion. Management took the time to listen. The phone-answering policy improved immediately. A simple, telephone answering data collection process produced the numbers in Table 8.3 that generated Figures 8.9, 8.10, and 8.11.

Table 8.3. Computer-generated orthogonal array and measured responses for a 2^3 design.

Analysis array			
Telephone lines	Time of day	Day of week	Total calls
1	A.M.	Mon–Tues	25
1	A.M.	Wed–Thurs	28
1	P.M.	Mon–Tues	24
1	P.M.	Wed–Thurs	23
2	A.M.	Mon–Tues	45
2	A.M.	Wed–Thurs	36
2	P.M.	Mon–Tues	49
2	P.M.	Wed–Thurs	38

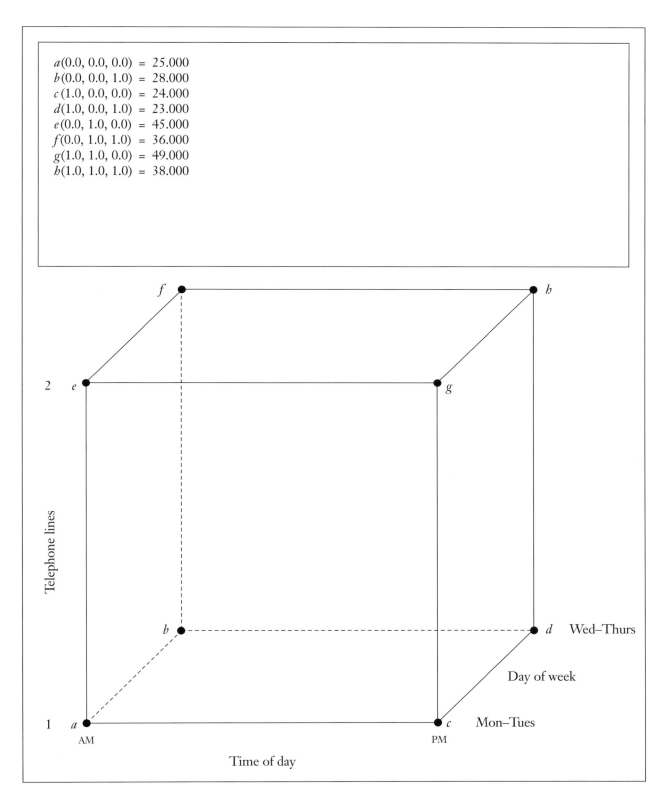

$a(0.0, 0.0, 0.0) = 25.000$
$b(0.0, 0.0, 1.0) = 28.000$
$c(1.0, 0.0, 0.0) = 24.000$
$d(1.0, 0.0, 1.0) = 23.000$
$e(0.0, 1.0, 0.0) = 45.000$
$f(0.0, 1.0, 1.0) = 36.000$
$g(1.0, 1.0, 0.0) = 49.000$
$b(1.0, 1.0, 1.0) = 38.000$

Figure 8.9. The cube helps a secretary explain a key process. The phone answering policy can be improved. Note that all of the largest values fall on the top plane. Line 2, the wrong listing, is the problem.

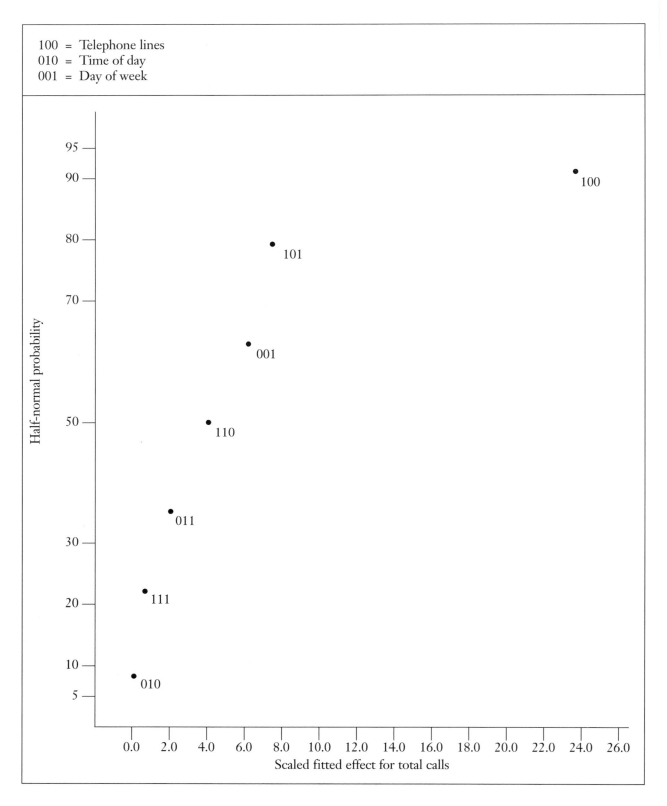

Figure 8.10. Telephone line is a main factor. Incorrect directory listing disrupted daily work.

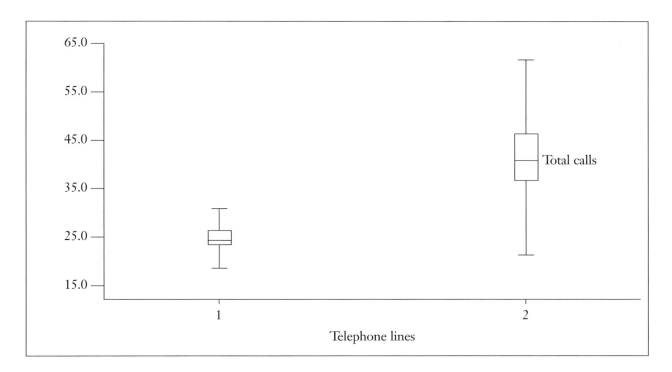

Figure 8.11. Line 2, the incorrect listing, is the problem. Constant interruptions stole time and productivity.

Line 2 was the problem. With management support, the team could troubleshoot the problem. A compromise was reached. Voice mail was used to screen and forward calls. Productivity and customer satisfaction improved.

Collecting, analyzing, and fondling data together is a work structure that builds interpersonal relationships. When a person's work is structured in this way on a daily basis, the results are rewarding. Designed experiments create a convergence of informed opinion. Convergence is a more powerful force than consensus. DoE helps everyone understand the problem, and, sometimes, the geometry of the experimental design helps everyone agree to the best solution in minutes.

When you take the time to learn how to use designed experiments, you will discover the fun, speed, and value of using fast-track experimentation on the job. Success leads to celebration and progress. Breakthrough achievements are cause for systematic and daily compliments. Fortunately, the analytic tools of designed experimentation and the system of compliments suggested by Steve deShazer create a force that overcomes the obstacles to change and improvement.[4]

Hematoma Study

An iterative series of qualitative studies in the cardiac cath lab on the occurrence of hematomas exposed the profile of patients who appear to be at risk. The profile developed with experimentation is: women over 180 pounds, who have a c-clamp applied for pressure. We learned that the presence of an anticoagulant in this patient population also correlates with a higher incidence rate of hematomas.

This original study was done by hand using the template included in this book. The DoE learning process related to hematomas continues. See Figure 8.12.

Factors ☞ Runs ▼	x *Weight*	y *Pressure*	z *Sex*	Response measure
1	−1 = ≤*179*	−1 = *C*	−1 = ♀	+ = *Yes*
2	+1 = ≥*180*	−1 = *C*	−1 = ♀	+
3	−1 = ≤*179*	+1 = *M*	−1 = ♀	− = *No*
4	+1 = ≥*180*	+1 = *M*	−1 = ♀	+
5	−1 = ≤*179*	−1 = *C*	+1 = ♂	−
6	+1 = ≥*180*	−1 = *C*	+1 = ♂	−
7	−1 = ≤*179*	+1 = *M*	+1 = ♂	−
8	+1 = ≥*180*	+1 = *M*	+1 = ♂	−
Orthogonal	0	0	0	

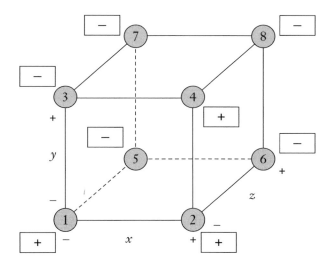

Place each measured response in the appropriate box. Do the values suggest a wider inductive basis for improvement action? Why or why not?

Effects formula: Add four points on a given plane and divide by four. Add four points on the opposite plane and divide by four. Subtract low settings, coded with a minus sign, from high settings, coded with a plus sign. Effect magnitude estimate equals the difference between averages.

$$x = \frac{2+4+6+8}{4} - \frac{1+3+5+7}{4}$$

$$x =$$

$$y = \frac{3+4+7+8}{4} - \frac{1+2+5+6}{4}$$

$$y =$$

$$z = \frac{5+6+7+8}{4} - \frac{1+2+3+4}{4}$$

$$z = .75$$

Figure 8.12. Design of experiments 2^3 worksheet for continuous improvement for hematoma study. Women weighing more than 180 pounds who had pressure applied with a c-clamp, rather than manual pressure, had a higher incidence of hematomas.

Post-Anesthesia Nausea Study

An iterative series of designed experiments in post-anesthesia recovery evaluated the degree of nausea in patients. The data indicate that younger patients tend to be more nauseous, on average, than older patients. The data suggest a paradoxical drug interaction between the administration of an antiemetic and the patient's age. See Table 8.4 and Figures 8.13–8.16 for the results of this study. Be cautious with your conclusions. With only four patients, these screening results could be due to random chance variations.

After the fact and from a distance, it is easy for a critic to say, "Well, I could have told you that." When one is immersed in the dynamics of a process, one is not always aware of the obvious. The Corrugated Copter examples illustrate how a team of well-intentioned people might attribute the effect to an incorrect cause. The surface area of the copters wings were the factor, not the pink color.

Designed experiments create real-time information when the information can leverage improvement.

Table 8.4. Computer-generated array for a 2^2 experimental screening study.

Label	Type	Levels	
Age	Main factor 55 under 56 over	2	Qualitative
Antiemetic	Main factor No Yes	2	Qualitative
Degree nausea	Response		
Analysis array			
Age	Antiematic	Degree nausea	
55 under	No	4	
55 under	Yes	3	
56 over	No	1	
56 over	Yes	2	

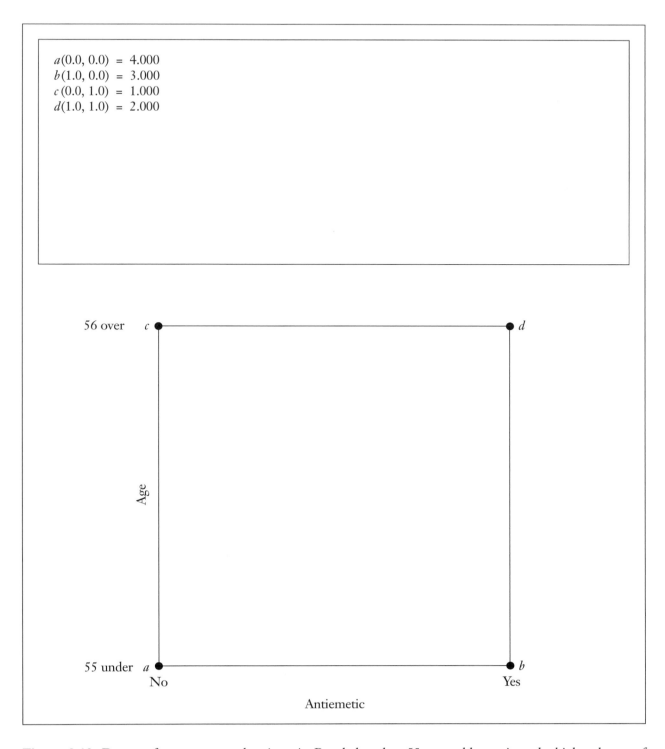

$a(0.0, 0.0) = 4.000$
$b(1.0, 0.0) = 3.000$
$c(0.0, 1.0) = 1.000$
$d(1.0, 1.0) = 2.000$

Figure 8.13. Degree of nausea: age and antiemetic. People less than 55 years old experienced a higher degree of nausea.

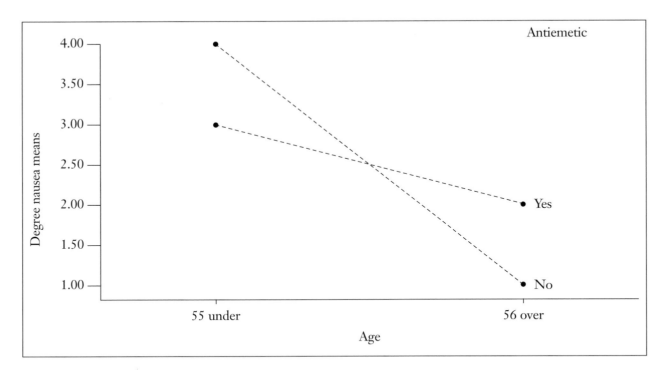

Figure 8.14. Interaction between antiemetic and age. Imagine that each line is the hypothenuse of a right triangle. The angles of error for each triangle are very different.

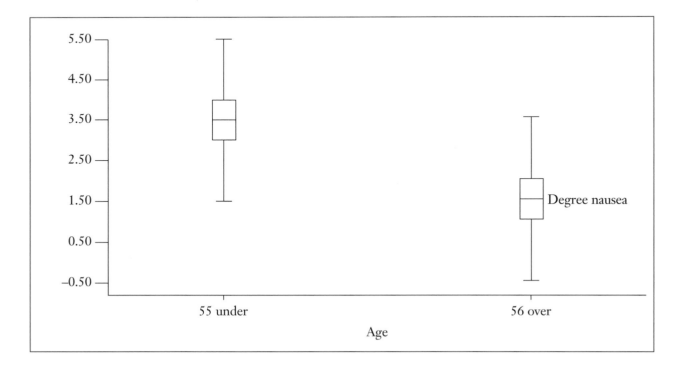

Figure 8.15. Dispersion: degrees of nausea by age.

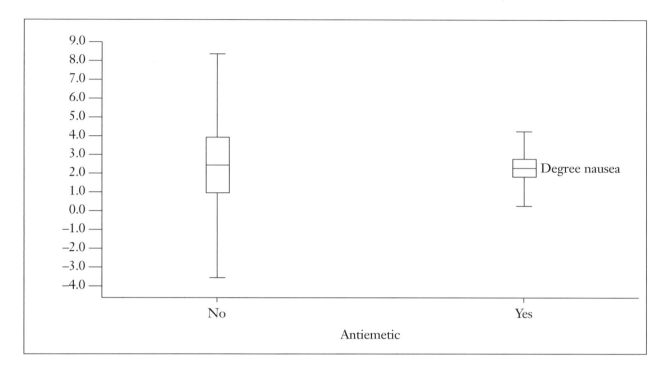

Figure 8.16. Dispersion: degrees of nausea and antiemetic.

These data were evaluated by the nurses, anesthesiologists, and surgeons to improve the quality of care and to reduce recovery time. Recovery-room time can often exceed $25 per minute. Maintaining the quality of care while reducing the recovery-room time can and does reduce costs by hundreds of dollars per case.

Do the math on your own patient population to determine what your organization could save. Note that it only took four data points to complete the series of experimental observations.

In an antiemetic study in progress at another medical center, researchers discovered that for their patient population, the presence of the drug was important. The type of drug, A or B coded minus and plus in the study, was not important. It is interesting to mote that a dose of drug A costs $0.48. One dose of the preferred drug B costs $16.50. By substituting an equally effective, less-expensive medication, $35,000 in costs could be avoided.

Surgical Case Turnover Time Study

An iterative series of designed experiments evaluated surgical case turnover time. Action to improve quality improved turnover times and lowered staffing costs.

The interaction chart makes several things immediately apparent. One person creates the most efficient turnover time for normal cases. A two-person turnover for normal cases slows the process down. Two people is the best staffing mix for extensive cases. A management decision to save money by assigning only one person to turn over an extensive case would be penny-wise and pound foolish.

Designed experimentation can be applied to any number of staffing puzzle problems. Preconceived staffing solutions are usually refined once insight is created with a good data analysis. Many times the data can be collected and analyzed in less than one week's time. Improvements can often be made instantly.

Note the simplicity and economy in this set of four observations. See Table 8.5 and Figures 8.17–8.20 for the results of the surgical case turnover time study.

Table 8.5. Computer-generated orthogonal array for a 2^2 experimental screening study.

Label	Type	Levels	
Case category	Main factor Normal < Extensive	2	Qualitative
Help	Main factor No Yes	2	Qualitative
Turnover time	Response		
Analysis array			
Case category	Help	Turnover time	
Normal <	No	15	
Normal <	Yes	20	
Extensive	No	30	
Extensive	Yes	25	

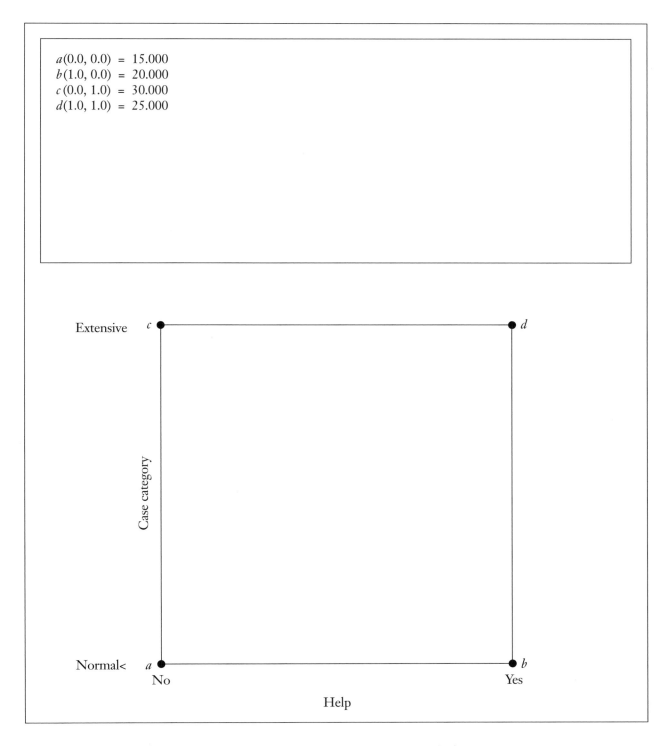

Figure 8.17. Turnover time staffing and efficiency study. Extensive cases take longer to turn over.

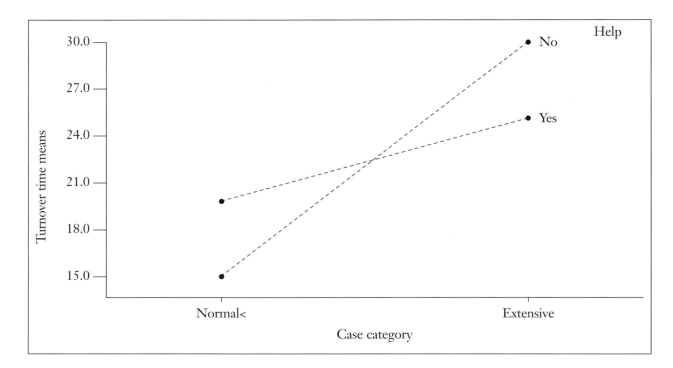

Figure 8.18. Staffing—case category turnover time study.

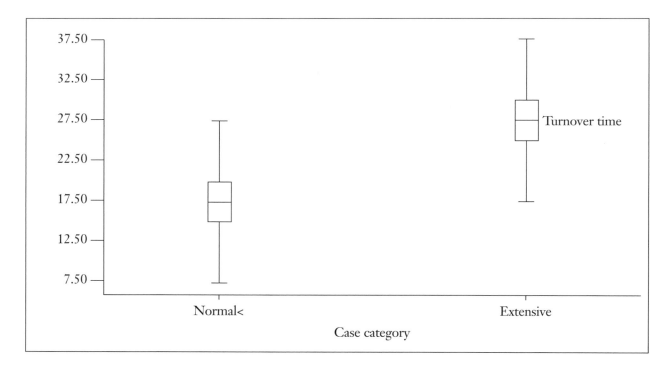

Figure 8.19. Dispersion of turnover time.

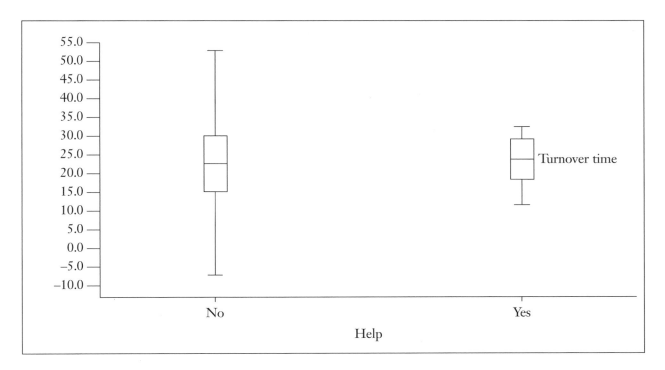

Figure 8.20. Dispersion of turnover time.

Nonsensical Experimental Results

A nonsensical experiment was created with invented data to illustrate how statistics can be abused. To the unwary experimenter without expert process knowledge, the following results may lead to a judgment that field trips are an important main factor that produces an improved clinical outcome. See Table 8.6 and Figures 8.21–8.24.

It is an unfortunate fact that statistics are often used, accidentally and willfully, to lie. It is possible to corrupt the integrity of a designed experiment. It is possible to collect data to prove a point; however, bias can never create understanding. The purpose of the quality sciences is to create understanding.

Once again, I encourage you to read *How to Lie with Statistics*. I recommend it to every person in your organization. Buy copies for your leadership team. Show them and teach your leaders how to use the more honest language of algebra, geometry, and quality.

Table 8.6. Computer-generated array that generated nonsensical results in a 2^3 experimental screening study.

Label	Type	Levels	
Nutrition	Main factor Underfed Overfed	2	Qualitative
Physical therapy	Main factor Low High	2	Qualitative
Field trips	Main factor No Yes	2	Qualitative
Negative inspiratory force (NIF)	Response		

Analysis array			
Nutrition	Physical therapy	Field trips	NIF
Underfed	Low	No	–2
Underfed	Low	Yes	–40
Underfed	High	No	–4
Underfed	High	Yes	–20
Overfed	Low	No	15
Overfed	Low	Yes	–37
Overfed	High	No	–5
Overfed	High	Yes	–42

In the process of teaching your colleagues how to use the language of quality, you will become a leader. You will discover qualities in your character you may have overlooked. You will find increasing amounts of courage to do the right things for the right reasons. You will prosper.

Designed experimentation will help discover what a wonderful process working together with your friends and math and science can be. The quality of your thinking will arch like a rainbow from your work. People will notice the beauty.

Truth and beauty in the workplace create happiness and high-quality health care.

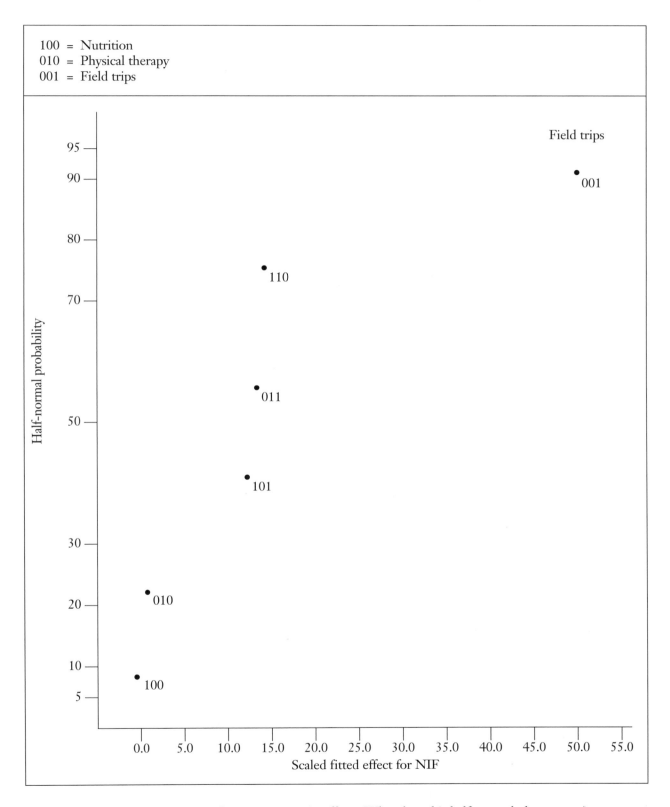

Figure 8.21. Negative inspiratory force suggest main effects. What does this half-normal plot suggest?

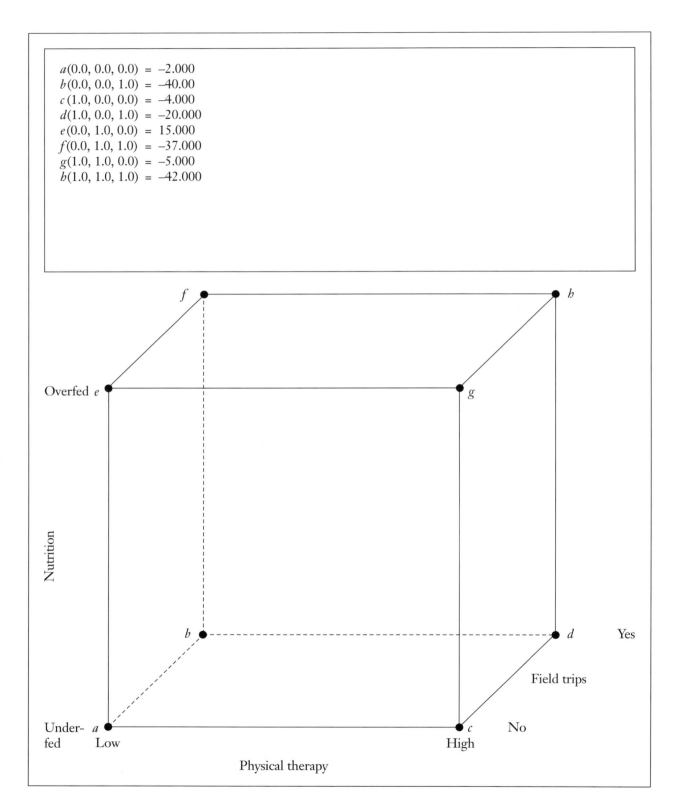

Figure 8.22. Ventilator patients and payors may be curious.

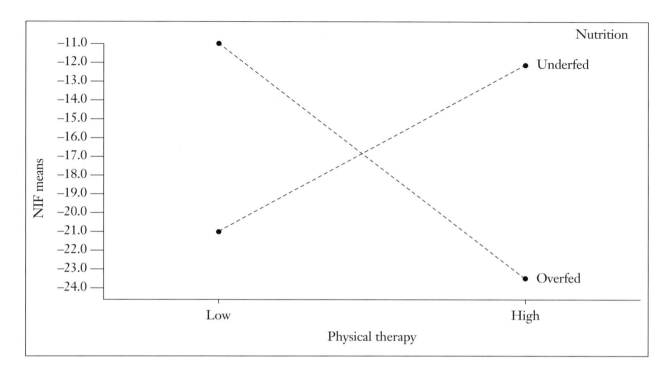

Figure 8.23. NIF as a response to physical therapy nutrition. What does this interaction suggest?

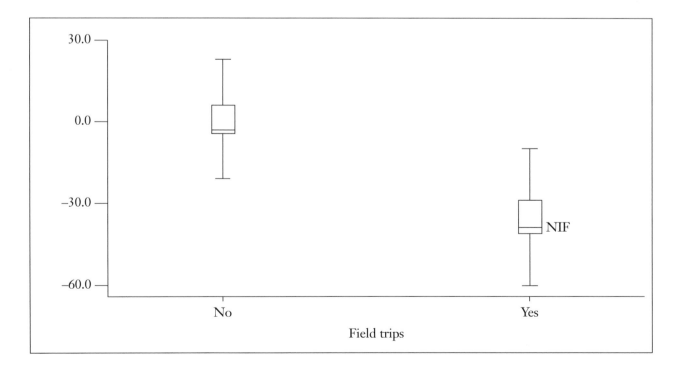

Figure 8.24. Do field trips contribute to the quality of care? In this case the answer is no, but a confabulated statistical answer could lead to a faulty conclusion that the answer is yes.

Summing It Up,
$\Sigma + \Sigma + \Sigma$

Experience teaches nothing without theory, but theory without experience is mere intellectual play.

— Immanuel Kant

I intentionally wrote this self-study guide with passion, optimism, conviction, and the happy laughter that productive work brings. And, yes, when I thought it might evoke additional thinking, I included personal and professional opinion. In short, I gave myself permission to have fun. I hope you enjoyed yourself too, because learning is fun. Science is fun. Believe it or not, statistics are fun. Statistics help us solve difficult puzzles efficiently.

I was reading two books as I was finishing the final manuscript for this work. Both books seemed to be written for me to read at just this moment. As you ponder the possibilities and opportunities that designed experimentation creates for your patients, colleagues, customers, and family members, you might enjoy reading them as well.

Surely You're Joking, Mr. Feynman by Nobel laureate Richard P. Feynman reminds me of Fisher and his reputation for sharing candid opinions with irreverence.[1] This *New York Times* best-seller is funny. Feynman has played with science and numbers for his entire life. Apparently he did his best work while he was "piddling around" with a wobbling plate at the Cornell University cafeteria.

According to Feynman, as he worked on the equations of wobbles, electron orbits moved with relativity and he drifted back into quantum electrodynamics. The diagrams and the "whole business" he got the Nobel Prize for came from the insight gained by observing a wobbling plate. Good old-fashioned fun can lead to amazing discovery!

187

Feynman writes about fascinating people he has known, scientists who could "just see the answers." This quality of visualized answers has an uncanny way of being able to be proven correct with experimentation and observation.

Feynman's reminiscences could have been made about the relationship Fisher and Gossett enjoyed for most of their careers. Gossett evidently had difficulty following Fisher's reasoning and logic. Gossett, quoted in Fisher's biography, said this about conversations with Fisher.

> It's not so much the mathematics, I can often say "Well, of course, that's beyond me, but we'll take it as correct" but when I come to "Evidently" I know that it means two hours of hard work at least before I can see why.[2]

Fisher revered Gossett for developing the t distribution. This invention rendered obsolete the restriction that a statistical sample must be "sufficiently large."[3] Even though Gossett "saw" the t distribution, Fisher doubted if he ever realized the full importance of his contribution.[4] The dissociation between theoretical statistics and the science of solving everyday puzzles with numbers still keeps too many statisticians and their students in the dark. Few realize the importance or practicality of Gossett's vision and Fisher's applications.

Thankfully, the history of scientific discovery is quite consistent. Over time, teachers and students simplify the information contained in an original, highly intellectual, visualized answer. Then, as Francis Bacon proposed, everyone uses the information to improve the quality of their own life.

J. Bernard Cohen's *Revolution in Science* sums up almost everything Fisher, Shewhart, Deming, and Box have reported about what it is like to lead the life of a revolutionary scientist.[5] Cohen sheds some light on how Claude Bernard, an early pioneer of experimental physiology, in all probability set back the use of applied statistical methods in medicine by more than 60 years.

Cohen makes interesting observations about the relationship between scientific revolution and the social revolution of democratic principle. He argues persuasively that the impact of the scientific revolution in the seventeenth century was and remains profound.

Traditionally, knowledge had been based on faith and insight, reason and revelation. The new science discarded all of these ways of understanding nature and set up experience—experiment and critical observation—as the foundation and ultimate test of knowledge . . . the humblest student could now test (and even show the errors in) the theory and laws put forth by the greatest scientist.[6]

Knowledge became democratic. Computers and telecommunications make it ever so much more so.

Personal computing power, user-friendly software applications, statistical theory, and the effectiveness of our nation's public and private school system have made it possible for the humblest patient to test and even show the errors in, or learn the wisdom in, the treatment plans prescribed by the greatest doctors and institutions. Depending on your point of view, this dispersion of (until now) privately held knowledge is usually either terribly frightening or incredibly reassuring.

Computer-literate young adults are entering the workforce with the ability, knowledge, access to information, and tools to test and show the errors in, or wisdom of, executive-level business judgments on their first day of work. Again, this availability of knowledge is usually either frightening or reassuring. Only rarely have I seen an individual's emotional reaction fall somewhere in between.

One future fact is clear. Any adult in any workplace who continues to rely on simplistic arithmetic answers instead of applying the principles of algebra, geometry, and sound statistical reasoning is in for a tough time of transition. Revolutions bring dramatic shifts in organizational power.

If you choose to promote the use of science and statistical reasoning (algebra and geometry) in health care, be prepared. Here is the outline I use to introduce quality science principles. With practice and luck, you may find that this sequence will work well for you as you work to convince your leadership team to buy into rapid, continuous, quality improvement.

1. *Learn to demonstrate the catapult experiment in 10 minutes. Demonstrate the power of designed experiments before you explain anything.* People learn by doing. The catapult experiment is fun

and fast. Buy a catapult or build one. The more I play with mine, the more I learn. Use the template in this book and a K'NEX® cube to show why the experiment and the analysis works.

Follow your catapult demonstration by flying 16 different paper helicopters. If you stand on a chair the flight times will be sufficiently long for a correct visual analysis. You will have everyone's attention when audience members understand they can make the correct statistical inferences with only 16 data points instead of 256. That 94-percent reduction in cost is appealing.

Use a K'NEX® cube to explain the tetrahedron in a fractional factorial experiment. Keep in mind that this demonstration is simplified. In actual practice the initial experiment would be used to screen all the factors. Additional confirmation runs would be completed to replicate the results. Science is a continuous process of experimentation.

2. *Show them how easy it is to use designed experiment software.* Have some relevant clinical or financial data preloaded on your laptop or desktop computer. Produce the statistical pictures. If you have to buy the software with your own money, do so. Or you can follow Betty Gwaltney's lead and program your spreadsheet application to automatically complete the template calculations provided in this book. Personal initiative distinguishes leadership ability.

3. *List the four primary benefits of designed experimentation. Demonstrate your point to prove it.* Remember, (1) Experimentation is economical; (2) Designed experiments let us evaluate multifactor interactions; (3) Experiments are fast; and (4) Honest measurement and analysis provide a structure for ethical, rational, well-educated, and profitable decisions.

Encourage people to use their expert subject matter knowledge. Help them array their own existing data from a clinical, financial, or operational process. Medical records or a handy series of monthly financial reports are excellent first choices.

Create a series of orthogonal arrays using the template in this book, your own programmed spreadsheet application, or your DoE software. Find data points that fit the orthogonal profile. Again, as Gwaltney showed me, the fastest way to complete this task is to query an existing database using a relational database application. Use an orthogonal sampling plan. Graph the output from each query on the appropriate statistical process control chart. Watch others' eyes pop out and their mouths drop open in amazement when you use the average values from each of the eight charts to complete a 2^3 screening analysis.

With practice, this demonstration usually takes about 30 minutes. So long as your historical data are in a rational and timely subgroup, you can plug them into an array with good results. You do not necessarily need to produce new data. If the data are not too old, you may be much more effective by using the data you already have in hand. Think orthogonally!

4. *Detail the logic of statistical reasoning.* Use the following sequence so your audience will convince themselves that algebra and geometry are better decision tools than simple arithmetic.

Use some humor and be considerate of your audience. Understand that this 15-minute exercise invalidates virtually every business decision model that health care organizations use. Most health care professionals are enthusiastic about this opportunity for bold improvement. Some become visibly shaken. Unfortunately, a few just get angry.

The unassailable logic of this argument returns us to this book's first illustration of the analysis of variance, Figure A.1, which is expanded here as Figure 9.1. Pythagoras's theorem and ANOVA are synonyms: $c^2 = a^2 + b^2$.

Use your good judgment in presenting your case. Some people whose job titles include or imply the word *analyst* are completely baffled by algebra. Many learned to loathe it early in life. The phobia remains, and your job is to help them learn to overcome it. These individuals may not be pleased with you or your ideas. People who do not value literacy, numeracy, and lifetime learning fear the worst. They may be quite correct if they infer that the discipline of statistical reasoning can force disquieting career and continuing education choices.

Use the bar graph sophistry examples in this book and pages 31–44 in *Success Stories in Lowering Health Care Costs by Improving Health Care Quality* (ASQC Quality Press, 1995) to illustrate your points. Use a white board with brightly colored dry-erase markers and a handheld calculator to show why the

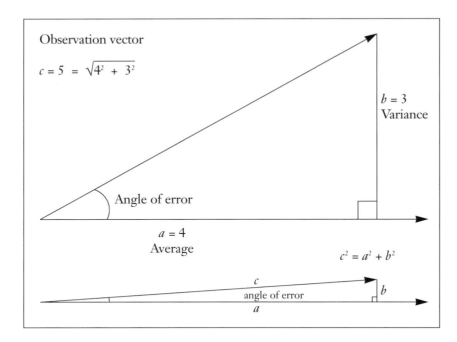

Figure 9.1. The length of the observation vector c (any series of counts or measures) equals the square root of the sum of its squared elements in this case four and three. The model can be extended to any number of dimensions. Completing an analysis of variance is as simple as comparing two right triangles. In regard to expenses, the process triangle with the lowest average a and smallest variance b is the best-quality process. The efficiency of target averages and smaller variances produces lower costs.

algebraic definition of variance is superior to the arithmetic definition of variance, as in Table 9.1.

Language competency, in English or algebra or geometry, can be and is judged by literate people. Fear or embarrassment may render these judgments silent, but the judgments occur nonetheless. When a leader summarizes his or her budget analysis with the conclusion that 1 = 3, he or she may as well wrap up the executive staff meeting by commenting, "As we seen from this here report, our workers jist ain't gonna git them pay hikes we wuz promisin'."

Obviously, there is a better way to lead an organization into the next century. Literacy and numeracy are essential. In the United States, every leader has an obligation to role-model bilingual competency in English and algebra. It takes a bit of study, but the credibility that competence adds to leadership is worth it.

Table 9.1. A comparison of the algebraic and arithmetic definitions of the word *variance*.

Variance defined by algebra, geometry, and the analysis of variance.	*Variance* defined by traditional quality assurance, cost accounting, and managerial finance.
The accepted language of analysis for all professional disciplines is algebra and geometry. ANOVA = Pythagoras's theorem; sum of the squares.	Ciphering is used in place of algebraic and geometric reasoning. A variance analysis is the answer to a single subtraction problem. Exponents are not used.

Actual observations^2
    = Average^2 + Variance^2
 	
$c^2 = a^2 + b^2$
 	
$5^2 = 4^2 + 3^2$
 	
Actual observations – Average
            = Variance
 	
    25 – 16 = 9
        9 = 9
 	
The square root of 9 is 3, the length of b.
 	
<small>In an algebraic or geometrical equation, both sides of the equation must be equal.</small>
	Actual outcomes or Actual cost
	    = Target average + Variance
	
	or
	
	Actual cost
	    = Budget average + Variance
	
	$c = a + b$
	
	$5 = 4 + 3$
	
	Actual cost – Budget average
	            = Variance
	
	Actual outcomes – Target average
	            = Variance
	
	    5 – 4 = 3
	    1 = 3
	
	<small>*Note:* As the numbers and the values of the actual observation measures increase, the size of the erroneous answer increases geometrically.</small>

The numbers in Table 9.2 are a distribution. Arithmetic only lets us calculate simple addition, subtraction, multiplication, and division problems. Algebra lets us solve more complex problems. Categorically speaking, the number 1 could stand for $1,000, $10,000, $100,000, and so on. The number 2 could stand for $2,000, $20,000, $200,000 and so on. For this example, we will just use the single-digit numbers with a dollar sign. See Table 9.3.

Table 9.2. Let's use five observations and five measures.

y
1
3
5
4
2

Table 9.3. Let's say the five observations, the five measures, represent monthly expenses for a department in your organization.

January	$1
February	$3
March	$5
April	$4
May	$2
Total monthly expenses = Σy	$15
Average monthly expenses = $\bar{y}$	$3

A variance, defined using arithmetic, is the answer to a subtraction problem. Using the arithmetic definition, we could conclude that the $4 upward expense trend from January to March equals an unfavorable variance. The $3 downward expense trend difference from March to April would be judged as a favorable variance.

Let's take arithmetic to its logical conclusion. Let's use the average monthly expense as a arbitrary budgetary guideline. Lets insist that the department manager hit this goal, claim credit for beating the goal, or get blamed for failing to hit the goal. Subtract the average from each month's expenses and see what happens. See Table 9.4.

Zero. This is the best answer arithmetic has to offer. A big zero, but zero none the less. The mean absolute deviation (MAD) is useless, meaningless information. We must reason at a higher level.

Table 9.4. Let's say the five observations, the five measures, represent monthly expenses for a department in your organization.

January	$1 – $3	=	–$2
February	$3 – $3	=	0
March	$5 – $3	=	+$2
April	$4 – $3	=	+$1
May	$2 – $3	=	–$1
Total monthly expenses = Σy = $15	Sum of the differences $\Sigma(y - \bar{y})$	=	0
Average monthly expenses = $\bar{y}$ = $3	Half the values are above average and half are below average.		

To get the correct answer we must sum the squares of the differences and calculate the sample standard deviation. Algebra to the rescue! Algebra lets us complete this calculation. The standard deviation is the universal measure of dispersion. It helps us determine whether or not any of these numbers represent special variations or whether they are all due to random chance in the system. Trends—improbable patterns—must be evaluated using calculation not confabulation. (Bear in mind that once you have done the algebra, you have also completed the geometry!)

Since the sample is small, lets use the algebraic formula for calculating the sample standard deviation. See Table 9.5. The first equation is the notation for sample standard deviation. The next equation plugs in our numbers from Table 9.5.

$$s = \sqrt{\frac{\sum_{i=1}^{n}(y_i - \bar{y})^2}{n-1}}$$

$$s = \sqrt{\frac{10}{4}} = \sqrt{2.5} = 1.58114$$

Table 9.5. Let's say the five observations, the five measures, represent monthly expenses for a department in your organization.

	$(y - \bar{y})$	$(y - \bar{y})^2$
January	$1 - $3 = -$2	4
February	$3 - $3 = 0	0
March	$5 - $3 = +$2	4
April	$4 - $3 = +$1	1
May	$2 - $3 = -$1	1
Total monthly expenses = Σy = $15	Sum of the differences $\Sigma(y - \bar{y})^2$ = 10	
Average monthly expenses = $\bar{y}$ = $3	Estimated sample standard deviation, s, = 1.58114. The mean, $3, ±2 sample standard deviations equals an estimated 95-percent confidence interval of –$.16 to $6.16.	

The variations month to month, the variance, are due to random chance. An individuals and moving range chart illustrates the distribution curve perfectly using three standard deviations instead of two. See Figure 9.2. There are no improbable patterns. There are no trends. The most reasonable thing a statistically literate person can say about the differences in this data set is that they are due to random chance.

5. *Use your laptop or desktop computer's financial spreadsheet program to calculate an ANOVA for two or more data sets in three minutes.* Use at least a year's worth of data so that you have enough for an honest analysis. Have your K'NEX® cube with you. The spreadsheet won't draw the pictures for you; however, by using a feature in the organization's favored financial software application, you will make a powerful point. The opportunity to apply an essential analytic element of DoE, ANOVA, is probably already loaded on the network!

Use the pictures in this book to show your audience the geometry in an ANOVA. Show why the sum of the squares is a synonym for the Pythagorean theorem. Show why graphical summaries of a designed experiment are so useful.

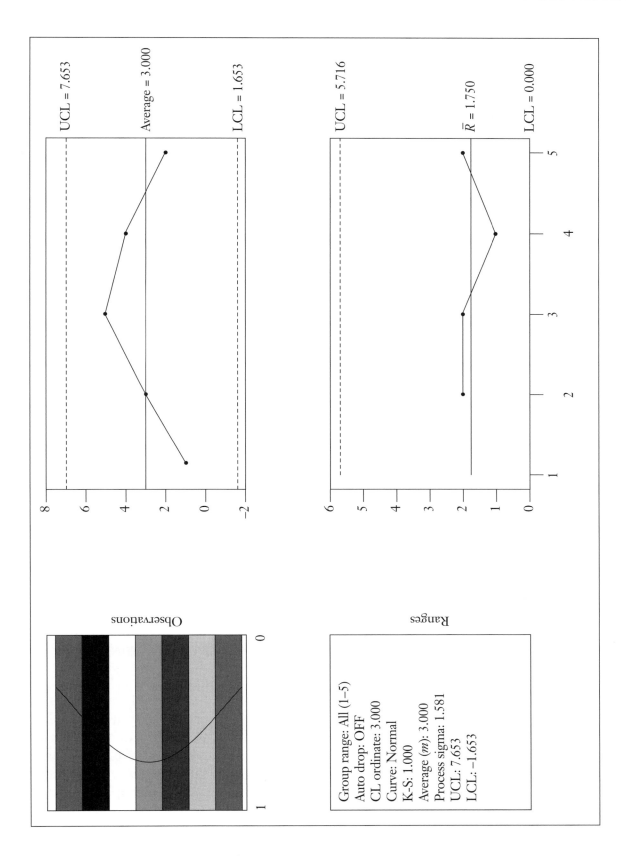

Figure 9.2. Common cause variation for monthly expenses. All data points come from the same process!

Give everyone time to consider the implications. Be persistent. Use the tools every single time you make a data presentation. You can literally transform the measurement and analysis standards for your organization within the context of a single presentation.

Implementing the improvements and maintaining consistency across all departmental and professional boundaries will take months and perhaps years of work. But once you have educated your team, there is no turning back. Over the long term, honesty and knowledge will win out.

6. *Turn to a colleague and ask for help.* You can't ask a book a question. No worries. If you want some rehearsal assistance, I am here to help you succeed. My e-mail address is sloan1@ix.netcom.com and I respond in as timely a manner as my schedule permits whenever a student contacts me. It will be my privilege to help you.

ICE CREAM CONES, TRIGONOMETRY, APPLIED SCIENCE, AND DEMOCRATIC PRINCIPLE

Anyone who has completed all of the math in this book deserves a reward. Celebrate. Buy a box of sugar cones, a box of waffle cones, and a half-gallon of your favorite ice cream.

Since you may want to develop an advanced level of proficiency with designed experimentation, I must tell you that excellence requires the quality science student to master complex number systems, trigonometry, and the concept of conic sections.[7] The formulas I included in this book's z table and t table hinted at this reality. I use this ice cream cone experiment in my advanced-level classes to defuse n-dimensional anxiety.

Take four circumference measurements at equal intervals on one sugar cone and one waffle cone. Start with their pointy ends (the *vertex* or *focus* in technical language) and move up toward the business end, the top of the cone. As always, the angle of error determines the variance. Calculate the sample standard deviation and reference interval for the two cones. (See unit 4, "Comparing Two Qualities.") Draw two right angles to compare the size of the variance. To confirm your analysis, nest the sugar cone inside the waffle cone or vice versa. It is a statistical fact: waffle cones are bigger than sugar cones! The size differences are not statistically significant; however, in actual practice I notice that everyone prefers the waffle cones.

My son Austin and I have replicated this experiment dozens of times. It works every time.

As you are eating your three-dimensional geometric model, ponder this idea. Designed experimentation, quality improvement, is a philosophy. Above all else, continuous quality improvement is a pragmatic combination of applied science and democratic principle. The principles of applied science promote democracy. Democracy is a beautiful idea that inspires me as I hope it inspires you.

Notes

Preface

1. Henry J. L. Marriott, M.D., *Practical Electrocardiography*, 7th ed. (Baltimore, Md.: Williams & Wilkins, 1983), 95.

Acknowledgments

1. Frank H. Netter, M.D., "Heart," page 54 in *The CIBA Collection of Medical Illustration*, vol. 5, edited by Frederick F. Yonkman, M.D., Ph.D. (New York: Colorpress, 1969).

Unit 1

1. M. Daniel Sloan and Jodi B. Torpey, *Success Stories in Lowering Health Care Costs by Improving Health Care Quality* (Milwaukee: ASQC Quality Press, 1995).

2. M. Daniel Sloan, *How to Lower Health Care Costs by Improving Health Care Quality* (Milwaukee: ASQC Quality Press, 1994).

3. Kathleen Stein, "Looking for the Sweet Spot in n-Dimensional Space," *Omni* 17, no. 8 (1995): 54–61.

4. George E. P. Box, William G. Hunter, and J. Stuart Hunter, *Statistics for Experimenters: An Introduction to Design, Data Analysis, and Model Building* (New York: John Wiley and Sons, 1978).

5. George E. P. Box, Søren Bisgaard, and Conrad Fung, *Designing Industrial Experiments: An Engineer's Key to Quality*. Madison, Wis.: The Center for Productivity Improvement, May 1995.

6. "Sir Ronald Fisher," in *Microsoft Encarta*. Copyright © 1994 Microsoft Corporation. Copyright © 1994 Funk & Wagnall's Corporation.

7. Joan Fisher Box, *R. A. Fisher: The Life of a Scientist* (New York: John Wiley and Sons, 1978).

8. Box, Hunter, and Hunter, *Statistics for Experimenters*, 552.

9. Douglas R. Hofstadter, *Gödel, Escher, Bach: An Eternal Golden Braid* (New York: Vintage Books, 1979), 49.

10. Box, Hunter, and Hunter, *Statistics for Experimenters*, 199.

11. Cecelia S. Kilian, *The World of W. Edwards Deming*, 2d ed. (Knoxville: SPC Press, 1992), 175.

12. Walter A. Shewhart, *Statistical Method from the Viewpoint of Quality Control* (New York: Dover, 1938).

13. Acheson J. Duncan, *Quality Control and Industrial Statistics*, 5th ed. (Homewood, Ill.: Irwin Books, 1986), 3.

14. Ibid., 4.

15. Thomas S. Kuhn, *The Structure of Scientific Revolutions*, 2d ed. enl. (Chicago: University of Chicago Press, 1970), 5.

16. Paul Starr, The Social Transformation of American Medicine (New York: Basic Books, 1982), 3.

17. Clarence Irving Lewis, *Mind and the World Order: Outline of a Theory of Knowledge* (New York: Dover Publications, 1929).

18. Box, Hunter, and Hunter, *Statistics for Experimenters*, 199.

19. Albert Einstein, *Relativity: The Special and General Theory* (New York: Crown Publishers, 1917), 123.

20. David Hume, *Hume Selections* (1748; reprint, Charles W. Hendel, ed., New York: Charles Scribner's Sons, 1927).

21. Sloan, *Lower Health Care Costs.*

22. Box, Hunter, and Hunter, *Statistics for Experimenters*, 31.

23. Sloan and Torpey, *Success Stories in Health Care*, page number.

24. Sloan, *Lower Health Care Costs*, 209.

25. *American Heritage Dictionary of the English Language*, 3rd ed., *s.v.* "quadratic equation."

26. Box, Hunter, and Hunter, *Statistics for Experimenters*, 43, 46.

27. Einstein, *Relativity*, v.

28. Lewis, *Mind and the World Order*.

29. W. Edwards Deming, *Out of the Crisis*, (Cambridge, Mass.: Massachusetts Institute of Technology, 1987), 328.

30. Box, Bisgaard, and Fung, *Designing Industrial Experiments*, Section 3.5.

Unit 2

1. *American Heritage Dictionary of the English Language*, 3rd ed., *s.v.* "gestalt."

2. *American Heritage Dictionary of the English Language*, 3rd ed., *s.v.* "algebra."

3. *American Heritage Dictionary of the English Language*, 3rd ed., *s.v.* "quadratic equation."

4. Box, Hunter, and Hunter, *Statistics for Experimenters*, 199.

5. Robert H. Lochner and Joseph E. Matar, *Designing for Quality: An Introduction to the Best of Taguchi and Western Methods of Statistical Experimental Design* (White Plains, N.Y.: Quality Resources and Milwaukee: ASQC Quality Press, 1990), 28.

6. Box, Hunter, and Hunter, *Statistics for Experimenters*, 5.

7. Edmund A. Gehan and Noreen A. Lemak, *Statistics in Medical Research* (New York: Plenum, 1994), 83.

8. M. Daniel Sloan and Michael M. Chmel, *The Quality Revolution and Health Care: A Primer for Purchasers and Providers* (Milwaukee: ASQC Quality Press, 1991).

9. Ronald A. Fisher, *The Design of Experiments* (New York: Hafner Press, 1974), 70.

10. Francis Crick, *The Astonishing Hypothesis: The Scientific Search for the Soul* (New York: Simon and Schuster, 1995).

11. Lightning Calculator in Troy, Michigan, supplies excellent catapults and quincunx boards that can be used to teach statistical process control and the design of experiments.

Unit 3

1. C. B. (Kip) Rogers of Digital Equipment in Marlboro, Massachusetts, is credited with creating this teaching metaphor.

2. R. A. Fisher, *Design of Experiments* (Edinburgh: Oliver & Boyd, 1935), 99–100.

3. Box, Bisgaard, and Fung, *Designing Industrial Experiments*, 1.2–5.

4. Walter A. Shewhart, *Economic Control of Quality of Manufactured Product* (New York: D. Van Nostrand Company, 1931; Milwaukee: ASQC Quality Press commemorative reissue, 1980), 313.

5. Box, Hunter, and Hunter, *Statistics for Experimenters*, 49.

6. Box, *R. A. Fisher: The Life of a Scientist* (New York: John Wiley & Sons, 1978), 126.

7. Ibid.

8. Robert D. Mason and Douglas A. Lind, *Statistical Techniques in Business and Economics* (Homewood, Ill.: Irwin, 1990), 422.

Unit 4

1. Box, Hunter, and Hunter, *Statistics for Experimenters*, chapters 6–7.

2. Lochner and Matar, *Designing for Quality*, 190–191.

3. Lochner and Matar, *Designing for Quality*, 190–191.

4. Deming, *Out of the Crisis*, 23.

5. Box, Hunter, and Hunter, *Statistics for Experimenters*, 171.

6. R. A. Fisher, Statistical Methods for Research Workers, 13th ed. (New York: Hafner Publishing, 1967), 15.

7. Box, Hunter, and Hunter, *Statistics for Experimenters*, 179.

Unit 5

1. Box, Bisgaard, and Fung, *Designing Industrial Experiments*, 1.4–4.

2. Box, Hunter, and Hunter, *Statistics for Experimenters*, 171.

3. Ibid., 176.

4. Box, Bisgaard, and Fung, *Designing Industrial Experiments*, 1.5-6 to 1.56-11.

Unit 6

1. Box, Hunter, and Hunter, *Statistics for Experimenters*, 300, 374.

Unit 7

1. Cecil Woodham-Smith, *Florence Nightingale* (New York: McGraw Hill, 1951), 101–103.

2. Box, Hunter, and Hunter, *Statistics for Experimenters*, 402.

Unit 8

1. Sloan and Torpey, *Lowering Health Care Costs*, 3–4.

2. Paul Starr, *The Social Transformation of American Medicine* (New York: Basic Books, 1982).

3. Darrell Huff, *How to Lie with Statistics* (New York: W. W. Norton, 1954).

4. Sloan and Torpey, *Lowering Health Care Costs*, page number.

Unit 9

1. Richard P. Feynman, *Surely You're Joking, Mr. Feynman* (New York: Bantam Books published by arrangement with W.W. Norton, 1989.

2. Gehan and Lemak, *Statistics in Medical Research*, 63.

3. Ibid., 64.

4. Ibid., 64.

5. J. Bernard Cohen, *Revolution in Science* (Cambridge: Belknap Press, 1985).

6. Ibid., 79.

7. Box, Hunter, and Hunter, *Statistics for Experimenters*, 201.

Index

Note: An "f" or "t" following a page number indicates a figure or table, respectively, as in 45f and 66t.

Courage, 152, 182
Crick, Francis, 52
Cube. *See* Experimental cube
Cubic equations, 30
Cultural change, 141–42

D

Days, in accounts receivable, 129–33,
    164. *See also* Length of stays
Decisions, poor-quality, 4–8, 157–58,
    167–68, 181
Deduction, 23, 72. *See also* IDEA
    cycle
Degrees of freedom
    ANOVA and, 97
    pooled standard deviation and, 103
    residuals and, 111
    t distribution and, 77–80
Deming, W. Edwards, 16f, 17, 23
    14 points of, 153
    on tampering, 25, 26
Democratic principle, 21, 27, 153–54,
    188–89, 199
Descartes, Réne, xiii, 30
Designed experiments
    advanced proficiency in, 198–99
    benefits of, ix–xi, 14–19, 147, 171,
        182, 190–91. *See also* Success
    compared to statistical process con-
        trol, 20–27, 48, 69
    compared to trial and error, 117,
        164
    essential elements of, 31–33
    problems with, 181
    problems with, preventing, 103–09
    steps to cost reductions with,
        154–66

steps to introduction of, 189–98
subject matter categories for, 66t
Design generators, fractional, 138
Determination, 152
Diagnostic related groups (DRGs),
    4–12
Dimensions
    n, 106, 198
    three vs. two, 22, 46f, 47f
Directed experimentation. *See*
    Designed experiments
Disciplined discovery, 13–19
Disciplines, as variables, 129–33
Dispersion, measures of, 69. *See also*
    Standard deviation; Standard
    error
Distance. *See* Catapult experiment
Distributions. *See* Normal distribu-
    tion; Probability distributions;
    t distribution
DoE (design of experiments). *See*
    Designed experiments
Dot plots, 72–73, 88f, 89f, 100f, 102f,
    103f. *See also* Residuals
DRGs (diagnostic related groups),
    4–12
Drug interactions, 174–77

E

Economics
    ecosystem analogy of, 162–63
    of scientific method, 14
Ecosystem analogy, 162–63
Effectiveness, 18
Effects formulas, 51f, 53f, 56f, 63f,
    64f
Efficient learning, 13–19